Praise for *A Clinician's Guide to Supporting Autistic Clients*

"As an autistic person I celebrate Dr. Marschall's *Clinician's Guide*, which fills a yawning gap in the literature of strength-based strategies leading autistic individuals toward fulfilling and productive lives as the rule rather than the exception. By shifting the paradigm toward supporting autistic and otherwise neurodivergent individuals with their characteristics, this volume is a must-read for anyone seeking deeper understanding of autism in the context of neurodiversity, and a shining example of extensions of good practice."

— **Stephen Mark Shore, EdD,** clinical associate
professor of special education

"Dr. Marschall has created an all-encompassing resource for both beginner and experienced clinicians working with neurodiverse individuals. It's bursting with actionable interventions that busy clinicians can implement immediately. The conversation scripts for navigating challenging topics with clients and caregivers are unmatched by any other resource. *A Clinician's Guide to Supporting Autistic Clients* will be required reading for all of my graduate students and supervisees!"

— **Katelyn Campbell, PhD**

"*A Clinician's Guide to Supporting Autistic Clients* is a much-needed breath of fresh air, offering supportive ideas and solid evidence of how to better serve an otherwise too often misunderstood clientele. From educating the reader about autistic neurotypes, to tackling hard truths of our field's history, to offering ways to do better by our clients now—this book is a delightful primer for clinicians who work with neurodiverse clients."

— **Amanda Cortese, MA, LCMHC, ATR-BC**

"As an autistic clinical psychologist who works directly with members of the autistic community, *A Clinician's Guide to Supporting Autistic Clients* reflects and informs many of my experiences. This book provides a comprehensive foundation for understanding the diverse needs of autistic clients, as well as pragmatic advice for providing flexible and affirming therapeutic interventions and resources. It is written in an engaging and informative manner, interspersed with tactful and clear scripts to support providers in effectively communicating with clients, caregivers, and other professionals regarding the theory and rationale behind the interventions and resources. This book is an easy recommendation to any provider seeking to enhance their ability to advocate for and provide effective and affirming care for autistic individuals."

— **Jared Kilmer, PhD,** clinic director,
Save Point Behavioral Health

A CLINICIAN'S GUIDE TO

SUPPORTING AUTISTIC CLIENTS

Over 100 Treatment Recommendations and Interventions for Creating a Neurodiversity-Affirming Practice

Amy Marschall, PsyD

A Clinician's Guide to Supporting Autistic Clients
Copyright © 2024 by Amy Marschall

Published by
PESI Publishing, Inc.
3839 White Ave
Eau Claire, WI 54703

Cover and interior design by Amy Rubenzer
Editing by Jenessa Jackson, PhD

ISBN 9781683737483 (print)
ISBN 9781683737490 (ePUB)
ISBN 9781683737506 (ePDF)

PESI Publishing
pesipublishing.com

Table of Contents

Introduction

The first American to be diagnosed as autistic, Donald Gray Triplett (known as "Case 1"), only passed away in 2023. Of course, autistic people existed before Triplett was identified, but the way we thought about this community was different before the twentieth century. For example, it is widely believed that stories of "changeling" children were used to refer to autistic or otherwise neurodivergent children whose behavior did not fit their parents' neurotypical standards (Leask et al., 2005). *Neurodivergence* refers to anyone with a brain difference that impacts behavior, emotions, and functioning in a way that falls outside of what is socially considered "typical." This includes anyone with a mental health diagnosis, brain injury, neurological difference, or neurodevelopmental diagnosis, including autism.

Part of the problem in conceptualizing autism is that, early on, autism researchers were exclusively nonautistic individuals, or at least those who did not identify as autistic (Bottema-Beutel et al., 2021). Those in power conceptualized autism as a problem to be fixed and emphasized trying to make autistic people stop being autistic rather than supporting the individual's needs. As a direct result, so-called therapies and supports for autistic people have historically focused on "curing" autistic behaviors and reducing the visibility of autistic traits. As the autistic community has become more vocal, many have shared that they found their "treatment" to be abusive (Sandoval-Norton et al., 2019), and studies have shown that these treatments increase autistic people's risk for developing trauma symptoms (Kupferstein, 2018).

Sometimes, neurodivergent people struggle as a result of existing in a society that is not built for them. In other ways, neurodivergence can be disabling regardless of the makeup of society. For example, some autistic people do not naturally develop the ability to communicate in a way that would allow their caretakers to easily understand them and meet their needs. Some have sensory sensitivities that make activities like going outside uncomfortable or even painful. These things might be disabling regardless of automatic accommodations. Either way, all people deserve the support and care that allows them to live their best lives, as well as the autonomy to express their needs and have them met.

Unfortunately, when it comes to supporting autistic people, the mental health field has not historically been affirming or listened to autistic people regarding what they want and need. Training programs either overlook the community's needs entirely or reinforce the idea that autism is a problem to be solved, pushing the idea that the aforementioned traumatic interventions are "best practice."

It is for this reason that, in recent years, neurodivergent communities have called for a move away from treatments that pathologize differences to neurodiversity-affirming approaches that meet their needs and offer support (Chapman & Botha, 2023). It is important to remember that there is not anything inherently wrong about being autistic. An autistic person who needs support for a mental health diagnosis deserves affirming care that recognizes their brain difference is a result of being autistic, with communication styles and therapeutic interventions designed with their needs in mind. This is not the same thing as trying to "treat" their autism specifically. In order to be an affirming provider, it is important that you take on this mindset before anything else.

What Is in This Book

If you work with autistic people and you want to provide an affirming, supportive environment for your clients, this book is for you. Within these pages, you will find background and education about the autistic community, the history of "best practices" for supporting autistic people, and the community voices and responses to these practices. You will come to understand how the autistic community has historically been let down and harmed by these so-called treatments, learn the link between masking and trauma, and become familiar with autistic burnout.

In **part I**, you will learn about the history of neurodiversity research and how it applies specifically to the autistic community. This first section presents a history of language and definitions around autism, autistic people, clinical diagnoses, "support" versus "cure," and the identified priorities and goals of the autistic community. The information here will allow you to develop background knowledge of autism assessment and treatment, as well as current information about community preferences. At the same time, remember to continue to learn and be open to changes within the community and in the field.

In **part II**, you will develop an understanding of how to be neurodiversity-affirming and how to best support autistic clients. However, autistic people are not a monolith, and individuals will each have their own needs. Therefore, the information in this section is merely intended as a starting point to help you recognize the autistic community's preferences and avoid traumatizing or further harming clients. You must always remember to prioritize the needs of the individual in front of you first and foremost.

In **part III**, you will find a collection of over 100 affirming tips, tools, and interventions developed from a neurodiversity-affirming standpoint that support the stated preferences of the autistic community. Since no intervention will be the right fit for every client and every situation, you can always tailor, tweak, or change an intervention based on a specific client's needs or the feedback they provide. Neurodiversity-affirming care is not a set of specific behaviors or interventions but an underlying philosophy of honoring each client's needs and respecting diverse neurotypes rather than holding "typical" neurotypes as superior.

The interventions in part III include options for autistic clients of all ages. Since many autism resources focus on supporting children, these interventions are specifically presented with the intention of giving you options to use with adult clients. That being said, if a client prefers "childlike" interventions or language, remember that this is okay. Whether due to neurotype or trauma history, some autistic people are drawn to things that many consider "childish" or "below" their age level. Honoring individual needs means not judging individual preferences so long as those preferences do not cause harm. Because of the need to tailor interventions to individual clients, many interventions in part III are open-ended and include educational scripts and philosophies rather than step-by-step techniques.

Finally, this book concludes with a list of resources about autism written by and for autistic individuals and from a neurodiversity-affirming perspective. It includes books, podcasts, blogs, and free educational websites. I have provided information about each resource to help you determine which one is appropriate in a given clinical situation. Of course, no single list can be fully comprehensive, but my aim is to give you a starting point. I welcome you to keep your own list and add more neurodiversity-affirming resources as you discover them.

As you read and use this book, there are three things to keep in mind:

1. I know a lot, but I don't know everything. This is not the be-all, end-all of autistic and neurodiversity-affirming care. Read this book *and* read all the other books.

2. Remember that autistic people are not a monolith. I did my best to reflect what the majority of autistic people have said they prefer regarding language, support, and so on, but if you are working with an individual autistic person who disagrees with me, defer to them as the expert on their own experience.

3. Change is inevitable. You cannot make a commitment to being neurodiversity-affirming and be done learning and adapting. Keep seeking knowledge from the autistic community and adjust your approach as needed as you gain new information.

My hope is that you learn how to address and correct harms from the field while showing up for your autistic clients in the most supportive and affirming way. That you unlearn harmful and problematic approaches. And, above all, that you base your practice on what benefits your clients, pulling from preferences and requests of the autistic community.

part I
DEFINING AUTISM

Autism and Language

Language matters. The way we talk about communities informs how we think about these communities. Utilizing the preferred terminology of the group you are discussing is also the fastest and easiest way to show support. However, language is always evolving, so you have a responsibility to educate yourself and keep up to date on the best practices and preferred language of the autistic community. While this section reflects what is most current, this information will become dated over time. In addition, while my discussion of language reflects trends and majority preferences, know that individual clients may deviate from these trends. When working with a client individually, it is important to center their voice and honor their preferences.

In order for treatment to be neurodiversity-affirming, it must reflect the needs, preferences, and language with which the client is most comfortable. Therefore, when meeting with a client for the first time, note that person's preferred language. You can either include a section on your intake paperwork or simply ask, "How would you like me to refer to you?" If an individual is most comfortable with terms that go against the majority of the community's preferences, that is okay. They have the right to their own opinion. Similarly, a client who previously preferred one term may change their mind. Make sure to update their individual treatment plans to reflect any changes in preference.

If your client is a minor child who is too young to indicate language preference, and they have an autistic parent or guardian, you can speak to the guardian about their preferred terminology and incorporate that into your work with the child. Similarly, regardless of age, if a client indicates that they have not thought about language or have no preference, it is best to err on the side of majority community preferences.

However, if the autistic child has only nonautistic (sometimes referred to as *allistic*) guardians, neurodiversity-affirming care would mean implementing community preferences. Some nonautistic parents want to impose their own preferred language onto their child. In order to be affirming, remember that the child is your client, and your goal is to support and elevate them as a neurodivergent individual. You can educate the parents about your language use and why it is important.

Identity-First Versus Person-First Language

When it comes to language preferences in the autistic community, most individuals prefer identity-first language (IFL), which puts the diagnosis, disability, or identity first (e.g., "autistic person"). This is in contrast to person-first language (PFL), which puts the person ahead of the diagnosis, with the goal of showing respect for communities by first acknowledging their personhood ahead of a diagnosis or disability (e.g., "person with autism").

Historically, many autistic adults indicated a preference for PFL because they felt it pushed back against the stigma that comes with an autism diagnosis. However, in recent years, many in the autistic community have indicated that they feel that PFL can be dehumanizing due to the implication that autism is something one "struggles with" or needs to be "fixed." IFL, on the other hand, can represent pride in the identity. Many autistic people also see IFL as more accurate because they see autism as a fundamental part of who they are, not something that can be removed or put off to the side.

A 2022 study by Autistic Not Weird surveyed more than 11,000 autistic people about their language preferences (Bonnello, 2022). Of those who responded to the survey, approximately 83 percent indicated that they use IFL when discussing autism. Additionally, more than 75 percent indicated that "autistic person" should be used exclusively rather than "person with autism," while only 15 percent indicated that either term is appropriate. Despite the overwhelming majority of autistic people clearly stating a preference for IFL, the American Psychological Association continues to indicate that PFL should be used in research and papers. Additionally, organizations that promote "autism awareness" without actually involving the autistic community continue to use PFL instead of IFL. Because many of these organizations promote "curing" autism, the use of PFL can be seen as an ableist dog whistle that shows that the speaker does not center autistic voices in their work.

Again, always ask clients for their individual preference and use their preferred language in their treatment. If they have no preference, or if you are writing about the community as a whole, your language must reflect community preferences in order to be neurodiversity-affirming. In other words, an autistic person can use the labels and language they are individually comfortable with, and you should respect these preferences on an individual basis. When referencing the community as a whole, use the current preferred terminology.

Because of the overwhelming community preference, this book uses IFL.

Diagnosing Autism

In order to understand the needs of autistic clients and develop appropriate interventions, you must understand what autism is and what it means to be autistic. The diagnostic criteria have changed over the years, and definitions have shifted further since the autistic community has found ways to make their individual voices heard. This text uses the diagnostic criteria from the *Diagnostic and Statistical Manual of Mental Disorders, Fifth Edition, Text Revision* (*DSM-5-TR*; APA, 2022).

In order to be neurodiversity-affirming, clinicians must keep in mind that *any DSM* diagnosis requires an individual to experience deficits (i.e., problems in social, occupational, or functional domains). However, some people exhibit traits associated with autism spectrum disorder—such as atypical sensory experiences, self-stimulation, or difficulty with nonverbal communication—but do not experience impairment as a result. These individuals may identify with the autistic community and self-diagnose as autistic while not technically meeting the *DSM* criteria for autism because they do not show the required "deficits" in functioning.

If you see autism as a neurotype that differs from the neurotypical mainstream, you can recognize that a given neurotype is not automatically disabling or disordered. Some clients might even see strengths in their autistic traits. At the same time, there is a clinical definition for autism spectrum "disorder," and many autistic people do find their traits disabling. In fact, many autistic people simultaneously see strengths from being autistic *and* are disabled as a direct result of being autistic. Both can be and are true. In order to be neurodiversity-affirming, you must honor these simultaneous truths as well as the individual experience of each client in front of you.

With this affirming perspective in mind, a clinical diagnosis of autism spectrum disorder requires that clients meet a specific set of criteria. First, they must exhibit "deficits" in social and communication skills, including an "abnormal social approach" and an inability to interact in ways that are deemed generally socially acceptable; nonverbal communication that falls outside of typical expectations; and difficulty making and maintaining relationships. It also requires "restrictive" interests and behaviors, including verbal or motor stims, strong need for routine, intense interests, and sensory sensitivities. The language is highly pathologized and presents these differences exclusively as deficits.

In addition, autistic traits have to emerge during the early developmental period and not be attributable to another diagnosis. Autistic individuals are then assigned a level based on their support needs, with level 1 autistic people "requiring support," level 2 "requiring substantial support," and level 3 "requiring very substantial support." A clinical diagnosis of autism can help an autistic individual get needed support and accommodations.

The language in the diagnostic criteria, of course, does not reflect a neurodiversity-affirming perspective and is deficit-focused instead. For example, many autistic people have a strong sense of justice and have difficulty letting something go if they know it to be morally wrong. This may be described as "rigidity" but is not necessarily a bad thing! Is it wrong to have high moral standards?

Additionally, many within the autistic community have pointed out the problems with the autism levels spelled out in the latest version of the *DSM*, which indicate the degree of support an individual is likely to require on a day-to-day basis. The autism levels replace the previous specifiers of "high-functioning" versus "low-functioning" autism, which were used to differentiate from "milder" forms of autism such as pervasive developmental disorder not otherwise specified (PDD-NOS) and Asperger's syndrome. In theory, these changes are intended to address the problems with old terms around autism, but in practice, they simply use different words to say the same thing: that autism is conceptualized as something that you can have more or less of, and less is somehow better. What's more is that autism levels are considered fixed, even though an autistic person's support needs can change over time. Someone with appropriate support may develop skills they did not previously have, and someone in autistic burnout might need greater support than they did previously.

While it is true that autistic people vary in how independently they can safely function, some of this is related to comorbidities and not autism itself. For example, autistic people are more likely than nonautistic people to have certain genetic disorders that can cause physical or intellectual disabilities, such as Rett syndrome, Down syndrome, and Angelman syndrome. If the higher support needs are due to a diagnosis other than autism, it is not accurate to indicate that their autism necessitates a higher level of support. Furthermore, many autistic people have varying support needs depending on the task at hand. For instance, an individual may be cognitively able to function independently but be prone to severe sensory sensitivities that impact their ability to complete certain tasks. Where would that person fall in the autism levels, which do not account for sensory symptoms? Autistic people do not neatly fall into the categories that this set of criteria suggests.

Regardless of an autistic person's comorbid diagnoses, genetic disorders, "level" or "functioning," and nature and severity of support needs, the following are *always* true:

1. Every single person is the foremost expert on their own experience.

2. Every single person deserves autonomy.

3. Every single person has the right to have a say in their mental health treatment.

Bias in Autism Diagnosis

Bias in Gender, Culture, and Race

Like many diagnoses in the *DSM*, the criteria for autism are predominantly based on research on White, cisgender boys from Western cultures. As a result, there continue to be disparities in identifying autism. In order for you to be a neurodiversity-affirming provider, you must be aware of potential biases as a result of this research and account for the variety of ways autistic traits can manifest.

When it comes to gender, an analysis of existing research supports the need for more studies examining the existence of gender differences in the presentation of autistic traits (Lai et al., 2015). Not only can gender impact autistic people's behavior, but the way providers perceive a client's gender can impact whether or not those behaviors are recognized as autistic traits (Lai & Szatmari, 2020). For instance, girls' special interests, like horses or fashion, are sometimes simply labeled as "girly things" instead of being noted as an autistic trait. Therefore, it is vitally important for providers to understand all the different ways autistic traits can manifest in relation to gender, particularly because trans, nonbinary, agender, genderfluid, and other people whose gender does not fall into their binary assignment at birth are more likely to be autistic than cisgender people (Warrier et al., 2020). Some autistic people's gender identity is linked to their autistic identity, and they may describe themselves as *autigender*.

It is not only gender that can interact with autism, as research shows that autistic Black, Indigenous, and other people of color (BIPOC) are less likely to be accurately diagnosed, take longer to be diagnosed, and receive fewer support services once diagnosed (Angell et al., 2018). There is an interaction of systemic oppression and access to resources that disproportionately impacts individuals based on race, ethnicity, and culture (Alyward et al., 2021). The diagnostic criteria for autism and assessment measures used for diagnosing autism are disproportionately based on research on White autistic children, which can cause false negatives when BIPOC children are assessed. Additionally, due to the medical and mental health systems' history of mistreating and abusing BIPOC individuals (particularly Black and Indigenous individuals), many of these families are understandably hesitant to seek services when they are struggling. An affirming provider must take an intersectional approach and understand how this impacts each client's experience with the system and accessibility of services.

Bias in Assessment Measures

Assessment measures used to determine whether an individual is autistic have the same biases described in the previous section. Many providers point to the Autism Diagnostic Observation Schedule (ADOS-2) as the "gold standard" in diagnostic assessment despite evidence that the measure tends to underdiagnose autism specifically in girls, women, and Black people (Kalb et al., 2022). With this in mind, it is irresponsible to use this measure to rule out autism with these populations.

Additionally, autism assessments historically rely on observer ratings more than other types of assessments, which is to the detriment of autistic clients. For example, the Conners 4 evaluates children and adolescents for attention-deficit/hyperactivity disorder (ADHD), and children as young as eight years old can provide self-report ratings about their experience and perception of symptoms (Conners, 2022). The same company produces the Autism Spectrum Rating Scale (ASRS), a measure that assesses for the presence of *DSM* diagnostic criteria for autism, but the ASRS does not have self-report rating scales, so children and teens who may be autistic do not have the same opportunity to provide information about their personal experience (Goldstein & Naglieri, 2009).

While collateral data can be helpful in psychological evaluations, relying on observer ratings over self-report perpetuates the idea that autistic people are unable to speak to their own experience. Of course, it is sometimes necessary to incorporate observational data in an assessment, as with the case of young children who do not have the insight to provide firsthand information about their experience. In these cases, it is appropriate and necessary to get information from parents, guardians, teachers, or daycare providers to supplement data about symptoms. However, as much as possible, self-report data should also be considered in all autism assessments.

Additionally, even though autistic children become autistic adults, and someone does not stop being autistic as they get older, test developers have not prioritized rating scales for autistic adults. Some adult rating scales for autism do exist, but they do not receive the same attention, research, and availability as adult ADHD assessments, for example. In order to be neurodiversity-affirming, providers must be aware of these limitations and promote affirming, intersectional, and competent assessments for autistic people of all ages.

Finding a "Cure" and Other Harms in Autism Treatment

Historically, research around autism diagnosis and treatment has focused on finding a "cure" for autism. As a result, too many providers continue to use "therapeutic" interventions that are aimed at training the autistic person to mask their traits and behave in neurotypical ways rather than finding appropriate supports and helping the autistic person be comfortable and live their best life. These interventions make the autistic person convenient to the nonautistic people around them but do not actually help the client themselves.

One such intervention is applied behavior analysis (ABA), which promotes compliance and teaches autistic people to conform to neurotypical standards. ABA instills the message that you must do what is expected of you even if it hurts you, leading clients to ignore their own needs and their body signals of discomfort. In fact, an analysis of ABA protocols found that such "treatments" can train autistic children that their autonomy does not matter, increasing their risk for abuse (Wilkenfeld & McCarthy, 2020). In this respect, ABA protocols present bioethical violations by their very nature (Wilkenfeld & McCarthy, 2020).

The problems with ABA therapy are well-documented, as an assessment of 460 autistic people exposed to ABA in early childhood found that approximately half had trauma symptoms, compared to approximately one-fourth of autistic people who did not experience ABA (Kupferstein, 2018). What's more, many autistic individuals who experienced ABA do not report having fewer autistic traits—they simply learned to hide those traits—and they found their treatment experience harmful and abusive (Sandoval-Norton et al., 2019). Treatment approaches that cause trauma responses directly contradict the ethics code of all major mental health professions that requires us to help rather than harm our clients.

To be neurodiversity-affirming, you must reject the notion that we need to "cure" people of their neurotype. For example, autistic people engage in repetitive behaviors—such as repeating certain movements, words, or phrases; listening to a song on repeat; or using fidget items—to help regulate their emotions and manage sensory sensitivities. This is called *stimming*, and often "treatment" protocols focus on eliminating this behavior on the grounds that it is "disruptive." However, when a behavior does not harm the client or another person, there is no clinical reason to reduce or eliminate the behavior, and doing so can instill feelings of shame as well as take away a healthy coping skill.

From a neurodiversity-affirming standpoint (and from an ethical and moral standpoint), it is not appropriate to discourage stimming altogether. An autistic person should never be shamed, ridiculed, or punished for stimming. At the same time, if a stim is causing harm (e.g., someone is head banging and at risk for injury), then you should certainly address the behavior, but the manner in which you do so is paramount. For example, an affirming approach to treatment determines how the behavior is meeting a sensory need and finds a safe, alternative behavior that meets that same need. It also identifies what stressors are triggering the behavior and works to eliminate those stressors in the environment. These are the two components to preventing injury from harmful stim behaviors:

1. Prevent triggers for these behaviors.

2. Find safe ways to stim when triggers are unavoidable.

Unfortunately, there is a history of dangerous and outright abusive "treatments" for redirecting harmful stims. Many of these approaches focus on using punishment to eliminate the behavior, which is ineffective and causes further stress. For example, the Judge Rotenberg Educational Center (JREC), a day and residential school and "treatment" facility in Massachusetts, uses devices that administer an electric shock to autistic children if an authority figure feels that the child is engaging in an unsafe behavior. The autistic community has condemned this practice, and the FDA previously issued an order for the JREC to stop these practices. However, the JREC sued the FDA to be allowed to continue administering electric shocks to autistic people, arguing that there was no other way to keep these children safe. (If you search for news about the JREC, you will see that despite their claims of prioritizing the safety of their residents, multiple autistic children have died in their care.)

Instead of determining what stressors were triggering head banging or other self-harm behaviors, the JREC claimed that they were "helping" reduce self-harm behaviors by shocking the individual until they stopped hurting themselves. In case this is not clear: It is not appropriate to administer electric shocks to *any* person to get them to comply with an order. Even if the desired behavior is a safe choice, you must find a nonabusive way to encourage that behavior. Shocking someone until they comply does not effectively teach appropriate, safe ways to cope with overstimulation or other triggers. Even if it did, what kind of message does it send? It teaches the client: "The people who care about you will hurt you for your own good." This increases that individual's risk for abuse in the future because they have been taught that it is appropriate for someone to harm them.

Therefore, if you want to be a neurodiversity-affirming provider, you must recognize the harm of emphasizing a "cure" for autism and understand the consequences that autistic clients experience as a result of living in a world that constantly sends them the message that they are bad, wrong, or broken. Instead, be aware that the existence of diverse neurotypes benefits humanity as a whole. Why would we "cure" or eradicate a neurotype that can present with its own set of strengths?

You must also reject the idea that people have to meet certain standards of productivity for their lives to be worth living. Regardless of a person's comorbid diagnoses, support needs, or level of "functioning," autistic people's lives are worthwhile, and they should not have to prove their value. The message that someone's neurotype needs to be "cured" or that their existence needs to be erased contributes to autistic people being at higher risk for suicide compared to nonautistic people (South et al., 2021).

Autistic Burnout

Burnout is a broad term that refers to the emotional, mental, and often physical fatigue and exhaustion that comes from excessive, long-term stress without relief or appropriate support. Autistic people experience a unique form of this known as *autistic burnout*. Although the autistic community has referred to this phenomenon for a long time, the term was first used in research in 2020 and is defined clinically as "a syndrome conceptualized as resulting from chronic life stress and a mismatch of expectations and abilities without adequate supports. It is characterized by pervasive, long-term (typically 3+ months) exhaustion, loss of function, and reduced tolerance to stimulus" (Raymaker et al., 2020, p. 133). This initial study found that characteristics of autistic burnout are distinct from other forms of burnout or from a depressive episode. For instance, autistic burnout is marked by "loss of skills," whereas depressive episodes do not typically include losing the ability to perform certain tasks. Additionally, while depressive episodes can be triggered by environmental stress, this is not a prerequisite, and autistic burnout is specifically brought on by the stress and trauma that comes with masking.

Autism researchers have previously noted a form of "regression" in which an autistic person begins to appear more autistic and/or has increased difficulty with functioning. Traditional definitions of autism and treatment recommendations align with this view: "We want this person to stop being autistic, but they seem to be *more* autistic. That is bad!" However, listening to autistic people who have experienced burnout gives us a new perspective and more helpful directions for future treatment. In particular, autistic adults who have experienced burnout often feel that the condition can be triggered by compulsory, continuous masking until they are no longer able to continue. (See "What Is Autistic Masking?" on page 49.) After forcing themselves to conform to behavior that is inauthentic to their true selves, autistic people become exhausted and enter burnout, as they no longer have the resources to continue presenting in neurotypical ways (Arnold et al., 2023). Note, too, that some autistic people experience regression or skill loss outside of burnout. Burnout and regression are two distinct occurrences, so it is important to ask each client about their experience and what terms fit with what they have been through.

A practitioner who is not neurodiversity-affirming may be tempted to push harder for conforming and masking behavior, but if that is what triggered the burnout in the first place, this will only make things worse for the client. An affirming practitioner recognizes the impact of masking and the stress of existing as a neurodivergent person in a world that expects neurotypical behavior. The affirming practitioner will help the client get their needs met in a healthy way.

Unfortunately, because clinicians only recently began acknowledging autistic burnout, there is limited information about appropriate treatment options. It is clear that burnout is marked by a depletion of energy, so rest is essential. However, how many autistic people have the space, support, and financial resources to fully withdraw until they recover? While research is limited, an extensive survey of autistic adults revealed the following starting points for managing, treating, and preventing burnout (Mantzalas et al., 2022):

- Increase awareness and acceptance of what autism is and what autistic people need. This includes addressing and fighting stigma and misinformation around autism.

- Recognize that autism is lifelong and not something that is "cured."

- Recognize the impact of being autistic in a world that expects neurotypical behavior on physical and mental health.

- Recognize the strengths that can come with an autistic neurotype.

- Provide education to autistic people about autism and help them identify their needs.

- Address the harms of chronic masking.

- Elevate and center autistic perspectives in all discussions about autism.

As our understanding of autistic burnout grows, it is imperative that you continue to follow the research on this topic and effective treatments for recovery. When vetting new research, assess who is conducting the research and whether they are focusing on autistic lived experiences in their outcomes. In practice, educate your clients with the information that you have, and collaborate with them in determining strategies that can help them.

part II

WHAT IS NEURODIVERSITY-AFFIRMING CARE?

Defining What It Means to Be Neurodiversity-Affirming

Understanding what autism is and how mental health care has traditionally harmed autistic people is the first step in providing affirming care. You must unlearn these harms and biases before you can implement sustainable change. Now that I have laid this groundwork, you can explore what it means to be neurodiversity-affirming and what this looks like in practice.

Being neurodiversity-affirming is not about using one set of interventions or doing and saying a series of specific things. Instead, neurodiversity-affirming care refers to the underlying philosophy behind your treatment approach. The same intervention can be affirming or nonaffirming depending on how it is used. When you take an affirming approach, you honor each client as the primary expert on themselves and their own life. While a therapist has expertise in mental health and knowledge about how to help the client on their journey, an affirming therapist acknowledges that there are two experts in the room and collaborates with the client rather than taking on an authoritative role. Together, the therapist and client determine what treatment approach meets the client's needs and honors the client's priorities, goals, and values.

For example, consider the use of exposure therapy, which has evidence backing it as an effective treatment for phobias (Böhnlein et al., 2020). A therapist with a client who presents with a phobia might recommend a gradual exposure protocol to treat those symptoms. However, some clients might feel that this treatment approach is not the right fit for them. Traditional, nonaffirming therapy would indicate that the therapist should push back on this, explore the client's "resistance" to treatment, and essentially try to convince the client to attempt the exposure anyway. An affirming therapist, on the other hand, might still explore why the client does not want to try exposure therapy, but with the end goal of identifying alternatives that are a better fit for that client.

Neurodiversity-affirming care is also about recognizing that our society, which prioritizes neurotypical behaviors and mannerisms, creates bias against neurodivergence. With autistic clients, it means rejecting the idea that the client is broken or wrong by virtue of being autistic. It means listening when the community shares that a treatment protocol has been harmful and changing your practice to reflect the stated needs of the community. It means appreciating that autistic people can and do have strengths tied to being autistic, and they deserve care and quality of life even if you cannot identify any strengths.

At the same time, affirming care is about acknowledging the client's disabilities. It is not bad or shameful to be disabled—*disabled* is not a dirty word. For some autistic people, the disability they experience related to their autistic traits is the result of living in a neurotypical society. For instance, an autistic person may have a hard time in grocery stores because the lights are so bright and the environment is chaotic. Their sensory needs might prevent them from functioning in that environment. But why is the grocery store laid out like that? It could be possible to create a sensory-friendly grocery store where that autistic person is able to shop for their groceries independently. Similarly, an autistic person who is nonspeaking and uses a communication device or sign language may be considered "disabled" in a society that labels verbal language as superior to other forms of communication. In an affirming society that recognizes alternative communication styles as valid, a nonspeaking person might not experience a disability.

There may be other difficulties that autistic people experience that would be disabling regardless of changes to their environment or to society. For example, someone with sensory sensitivities may become overstimulated easily by sunlight. This person might experience a disability regardless of changes to their environment because the sun will not cease to exist without taking out all of humanity. A neurodiversity-affirming therapist holds all of these truths simultaneously and honors the unique experience of each client they encounter.

Challenging Preconceived Notions

Many training programs continue to promote nonaffirming concepts, including the idea that when clients decline specific interventions, this represents "resistance" to be fixed rather than communication about the client's needs. Clinicians in training might learn that they are the only expert in the room without acknowledging the client's expertise on their own life or their autonomy to speak to their own treatment plan.

Even students who receive training in affirming care might not get accurate information about autism, or any information about autism. In my own program, I recall taking two years of psychological assessment, none of which discussed how to identify autism—my training in autism evaluations all took place in my predoctoral internship or after graduation. I recall a professor stating that there was no need to understand autism unless you specialized in it because so few people are autistic and "autistic people don't benefit from therapy because they can't engage in the process." This was a doctoral-level, tenured professor.

If professionals do not have accurate information about autism, how can the general public be expected to know? Lack of education around autism is a big part of why many autistic people do not realize they are autistic until later in life. Stereotypes and media misrepresentation contribute to this. As a provider, you have a responsibility to help your clients get accurate and helpful information and to challenge inaccurate representation you see in the world. That means you will need to unlearn false or harmful information. It is not shameful to learn that you were wrong in the past—know better and do better now. Learning is a process, and no one gets to a point where they know everything and have nothing new to learn. You can and ought to continue to change your worldview based on new information as it arises.

Respecting Autonomy

Historically, autistic people's autonomy has been stripped away or denied, which is a practice that continues today. Autistic people continue to be dehumanized, to be declared "incompetent," and to have their rights revoked, sometimes supposedly for their "own good" and sometimes due to blatantly ableist policies. There is strong evidence that autistic people experience loss of autonomy due to stigma, discrimination, and interference from nonautistic people (Späth & Jongsma, 2020). The following examples are intended as a sampling, and this list is by no means exhaustive:

- The state of North Dakota requires all healthcare and mental health providers to register autistic clients (anyone they diagnose as autistic or anyone who discloses they were diagnosed by another provider) in a database run by the state health department. The report includes the client's full name and contact information, other diagnoses the individual has, what supportive services the person receives, and specific behaviors the person exhibits. Providers who do not comply with the database can be fined up to $1,000 per client and have their license revoked. Clients and their legal guardians are not allowed to opt out of the database. The health department has not provided a public update about their use of this information since 2017 (North Dakota Department of Health and Human Services, 2022). In other words—if you or your child were diagnosed as autistic in North Dakota, the diagnostician would be legally required to put you on a government list.

- While some autistic people struggle to function independently and may benefit from additional support, many states put disabled people under guardianship or conservatorship, meaning that they are not permitted to control their finances or make their own decisions. This practice can lead to abuse and denies autonomy. Autistic adults are thus at risk for conservatorships due to their autism diagnosis (Autistic Self Advocacy Network, 2020).

- Autistic people face medical discrimination and ableism, including mistreatment by providers and denial of care, sometimes being rejected for organ transplants on the basis of an autism diagnosis (Stein, 2019).

- Disabled parents, including autistic parents with an official diagnosis, are denied custody of their children at a disproportionate rate (Powell, 2014).

These systems go out of their way to deny autistic people autonomy, privacy, and other rights, implementing more severe restrictions than is necessary. Unfortunately, these systems are often praised for "protecting" autistic people, who are presumed to not have the competency to make their own decisions.

Autistic people are left unable to speak for themselves, with nonautistics assuming they know better and the autistic community's values and needs ignored.

Affirming care respects autonomy and promotes independence and self-actualization as much as possible. This does not mean that certain autistic individuals will never have a guardianship or conservatorship, or that every autistic parent will automatically get full custody of their children. However, it means being aware of the ableist systems that discriminate against autistic adults and assume incompetence without evidence. It means implementing guardianship if that is the only way to get the autistic adult the support they need and engaging in ongoing oversight of the guardianship agreement to monitor for possible abuse. And it definitely means not putting autistic people on a government list or denying them healthcare on the basis of an autism diagnosis.

In the context of mental health treatment, this means that you collaborate with the client and prioritize their self-stated goals for treatment. You not only respect your client's autonomy in their treatment, but you teach them that they have the right to autonomy so they can assert themselves in other situations.

Understanding the Intersectional Context

As discussed earlier, an individual's other identities play a role in their experience of autism, and this is a key component of an intersectional approach to neurodiversity-affirming care. For example, some Indigenous cultures consider sustained eye contact to be disrespectful, so discomfort with eye contact is not seen as a problem. Additionally, it has been well-established that Black individuals in the United States experience police brutality at a disproportionate rate compared to their White counterparts, with Black autistic individuals at even higher risk for this type of violence at the hands of law enforcement (Hutson et al., 2022). These are just a few examples of how identities overlap to impact someone's experience in the world.

Affirming providers continuously educate themselves on these intersections to understand all aspects of a client's identity. While it is impossible to be an expert on every aspect of every client all the time, you can make efforts to be as aware as possible. A provider who avoids ableist microaggressions but does not address racism, sexism, transphobia, homophobia, or other forms of discrimination still does a harmful disservice to their clients. It is essential to make time to learn about the experiences of all different groups and how autistic people from these groups experience the intersections of their identities. While the client is the expert on their personal experience, be mindful that you do not put the burden on them to educate you about the broader, systemic context of their experience.

Be aware, too, that clients may experience marginalization within the autistic community. For example, autistic people who either do not speak English or for whom English is not their first language have experienced criticism from the community when referring to themselves using person-first language because their native language does not have a word for "autistic." Respecting individual experiences and identities includes acknowledging cultural and language differences for autistic people around the world rather than focusing only on one subset of the autistic community.

Implementing Trauma-Informed Care

In the medical and mental health worlds, the term *trauma-informed care* refers to care that "understands and considers the pervasive nature of trauma and promotes environments of healing and recovery rather than practices and services that may inadvertently retraumatize" (University at Buffalo, 2022). Practitioners who provide trauma-informed services are aware that, while not everyone has trauma history, a given client may have a history of trauma, and providers can use this awareness to take steps to prevent retraumatization or future trauma in the treatment setting.

We unfortunately cannot guarantee that nothing will be triggering for our clients. Trauma can be complex, and each person's experience is unique. As such, anything and everything has the potential to be a trauma trigger for someone, somewhere. Additionally, some procedures are inherently stressful and can be retraumatizing for many individuals, but this does not necessarily mean it is healthy or appropriate to get rid of the procedure all together. For example, a trauma-informed gynecologist would not say that any client with a sexual abuse history should simply forgo a pelvic exam, but they would take steps to help the client feel as safe and comfortable as possible for the procedure.

Since anything could be a trauma trigger, trauma-informed care is not about eliminating potentially triggering situations, procedures, or language; instead, it focuses on addressing triggers appropriately as they arise. For example, if a client is triggered by a specific word, the therapist notes this information when they receive it and avoids using that term around that particular client in the future. What's more, trauma-informed care goes beyond the therapist's behavior in session and involves trauma awareness and sensitivity at all levels of the organization (Bloom, 2010). For example, a trauma-informed office has all administrative and client-facing staff undergo training for providing trauma-informed care, and it conducts trauma screenings in a respectful, safe manner on all clients. Essentially, trauma-informed care is baked into all levels and present in all interactions.

Like neurodiversity-affirming care, trauma-informed care is not one set of interventions but rather an underlying philosophy behind treatment. At its core, trauma-informed care shifts the question from "What is wrong with this person?" to "What has happened to this person?" While neurodiversity-affirming care honors all neurotypes as valid, trauma-informed care takes active steps to be aware of potential triggers or retraumatizing procedures. Both prioritize client autonomy and recognize the client's role as the expert on their own life.

Existing as a neurodivergent person in a world that expects you to be neurotypical is stressful and can be traumatic. In fact, research shows that between 32 percent (Haruvi-Lamdan et al., 2020) and 60 percent (Rumball et al., 2020) of autistic people experience symptoms of posttraumatic stress disorder (PTSD) at some point in their lives, compared to 4 to 8 percent of the general population. Autistic people are also at higher risk than the rest of the population for depression and suicidal ideation and behavior, which can be connected to trauma or chronic stress. Therefore, a trauma-informed approach to care is essential in making care neurodiversity-affirming.

Amplifying Diverse Voices in the Autistic Community

Every community is diverse, including the autistic community. Just like autistic traits can present in a wide variety of ways, the autistic community is filled with people from different backgrounds, with different needs, and with different values and priorities. For example, as I discussed earlier, not all autistic people are in agreement about IFL versus PFL. A large majority certainly do prefer IFL, so texts about autistic people should reflect that language preference, but practitioners do not need to correct a client in their office who self-identifies as "having autism."

No one speaks for the entire autistic community or even for one subset of that community. That is why at the end of this book, I've provided a list of other resources that you should consider when implementing a neurodiversity-affirming practice. As a single author, I can only provide one perspective. With this in mind, when amplifying community perspectives, make sure that you consider a variety of sources and that you ensure those sources truly reflect the autistic community. Many organizations claim to exist to help autistic people but do not actually have any autistic people in leadership positions (or only have one). Consider:

1. Was this resource developed by autistic people?

2. What input from autistic people was considered in its development?

3. What have autistic people said about this?

4. What are this organization's goals for the autistic community?

5. Does this organization (or does the developer of this resource) prioritize autistic feedback?

6. Do they seek and implement feedback from a diverse group of autistic people (different support needs, language abilities, cognitive skills, races and ethnicities, genders, comorbid disabilities, and so forth)?

These questions can help you determine whether a resource is neurodiversity-affirming and whether it actually helps autistic people.

part III

A COLLECTION OF NEURODIVERSITY-AFFIRMING INTERVENTIONS

The first two parts of this book demonstrated some of the problems present in the existing mental health system and explained why those systems are problematic and harmful. It is important to understand the history, discrimination, and trauma that comes from nonaffirming care in order to be aware of the biases and components of your training that may have left you ignorant or uninformed. It is okay to acknowledge that you made mistakes when you did not know better. This is part of doing better now.

Armed with the knowledge of what it means to be neurodiversity-affirming and the research supporting the need for this kind of care, you can begin to implement this approach in your sessions with clients. To help you get started, this next section provides a myriad of specific interventions, tools, and scripts you can use in your sessions with autistic clients. These interventions cover the following topics:

- Client psychoeducation

- Sensory stimulation (movement, music and sound, tactile)

- Interoception and mindfulness

- Food-based sensitivities

- Demand avoidance/drive for autonomy

- Communication

- Trauma

- Autistic burnout

While some of the interventions include suggested age ranges, these are intended only as guidelines and not as hard-and-fast rules for what is or is not "appropriate" with a given client. If a client is interested in an approach that is indicated for an older age range, use your clinical judgment to determine whether it is developmentally appropriate or can be modified to be appropriate. Additionally, if a client enjoys "childlike" things, that is okay! You are never too old for something if you find that it benefits you. In fact, many coping skills that might be seen as childish can be safe, appropriate alternatives to unsafe substance use or self-harm behaviors.

While this book focuses on creating a neurodiversity-affirming experience for autistic clients specifically, this treatment approach can benefit clients of any neurotype, especially those who divert from what is defined by society as "neurotypical." Additionally, if a client exhibits autistic traits, relates to autistic experiences, or self-identifies as autistic without an official diagnosis from a provider, they can still benefit from these affirming interventions. It is important to remember that many autistic people are undiagnosed. For example, a survey conducted by Autistic Not Weird found that about half of autistic people and their caregivers felt that an official diagnosis was inaccessible (Bonnello, 2022). The survey asked autistic people and their caregivers about their perception of how accessible it is to obtain an autism diagnosis, with details about their perceptions outlined in the following graphs.

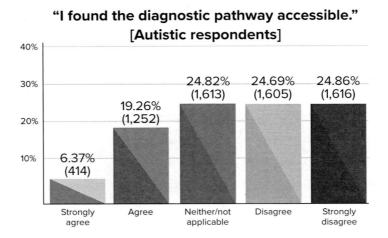

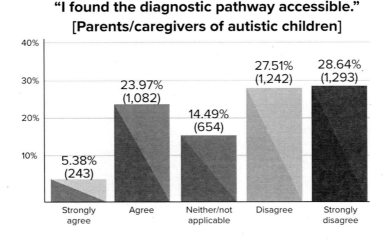

From *Results and Analysis of the Autistic Not Weird 2022 Autism Survey* (https://autisticnotweird.com/autismsurvey).
Copyright © 2022 by Chris Bonnello. Reprinted with permission.

Affirming Care: The What Versus the How

Before exploring specific interventions, remember that neurodiversity-affirming care is less about what you do in your sessions and more about your underlying affirming approach to care. The same intervention can be affirming or nonaffirming depending on how you use it. Honoring clients' autonomy means giving them the right to decline any intervention with which they are uncomfortable or modifying an intervention based on their feedback.

Additionally, neurodiversity-affirming care often requires breaking boxes you have previously perceived around your interventions as well as your clients. Just as each autistic person is unique and has their own therapeutic and support needs, most of these interventions do not neatly fit into one category. You will notice that, although this book has separate sections for sensory interventions, mindfulness interventions, and so forth, many interventions tap into more than one category. I have sorted them to the best of my ability into the primary or most prevalent category for your convenience and have noted overlaps where appropriate.

When considering interventions found in other sources, it's important to remember that some interventions cannot be neurodiversity-affirming by nature of the intervention itself. For instance, an intervention aimed at teaching an autistic client to stop stimming altogether cannot be affirming. A client may need support in addressing environmental triggers for harmful stims, or they may need to practice nonharmful stimming behaviors, but an attempt to make them stop stimming altogether would be contraindicated. If you wonder whether you should address a behavior like stimming in therapy, ask yourself the following:

1. Is the behavior harming the client?

2. Is the behavior harming another person or animal?

3. Is the behavior causing damage to property that cannot be easily replaced?

If the answer to all three of these questions is no, then the behavior is not problematic. Sometimes parents become concerned that their child will be bullied or teased for stimming behavior, but an affirming approach would involve encouraging the parents to advocate with the school to teach students to be kind and respectful of various needs rather than requiring the autistic child to conform to neurotypical standards. Yes, discouraging the behavior might mean the autistic child's peers do not notice that specific behavior, but this sends the autistic child the same message as the bullying: that they are bad, are wrong, and need to change who they are in order to be accepted.

In addition to remaining aware of what behaviors to address or not address, when it comes to collecting interventions for your neurodiversity-affirming care toolbox, make sure that you stay flexible, and be prepared to modify interventions for each client based on their needs, preferences, and feedback. Even the act of receiving feedback from clients and incorporating it teaches the client that their comfort, their voice, and their needs matter. It tells them that they have the right to be assertive, and they can say no to things that do not work for them. This fosters confidence, resilience, and self-esteem, and it reduces the risk for future abuse.

Neurodiversity-affirming care is about the *why* rather than the *what*. Keep this in mind when choosing interventions to offer to your clients, and you will foster positive growth and change. In addition, because neurodiversity-affirming care is about an underlying philosophy rather than set activities, some of the interventions in this book have general guidelines rather than specific instructions. Use these guidelines as a starting point in your work with clients.

Creating a Sensory-Friendly Office Space

Have you ever entered a space and felt immediately uncomfortable? Perhaps this discomfort arose because of the lighting, the colors, or a general feeling you had about the space. How long did it take you to settle into the space and alleviate your discomfort? If your sensory experience falls under what is considered "typical," this feeling may be unfamiliar, or you might wonder why it would take someone more than a few minutes to become comfortable and habituate to the environment.

For many autistic people, though, sensory processing difficulties can make some spaces unbearable. For example, although usually quiet, electricity has noise. Some autistic people can hear electricity (Local Government Association, 2023) and may be bothered by the sound made by the lights, even if you cannot perceive it. Additionally, many autistic people do not habituate (stop noticing a sensory experience over time) in the same way as nonautistic people (Kleinhans et al., 2009). If your office is not a sensory-friendly environment, autistic clients may struggle to feel at ease. They may even be unable to come into the space.

Since each person has unique sensory needs, there is unfortunately not one simple checklist to create a fully sensory-friendly space, but there are things you can do to make your office a safe place for autistic clients with sensory issues, which I outline in the following paragraphs. It is okay if you do not have the ability to implement every suggestion noted here, of course, but taking these steps can help autistic clients feel safe and be themselves in your office. Effort counts, too, so if you are not allowed or do not have the means to get new seating, make changes to the lighting, and so forth, making small changes that are within your control can show your autistic clients that you prioritize their needs and want them to be safe and comfortable. The most important aspect is to make your office adaptable and modifiable, and to communicate to clients that they can also make tweaks to make themselves comfortable.

Adjustable Lights

Since some autistic people can hear the buzzing of electricity that others do not perceive or notice, it can be helpful to adjust the lighting in your space. Incandescent and LED light bulbs tend to be quieter but can still make noise, so clients who can hear electricity might prefer to turn the lights off altogether to reduce this sound. In addition, many autistic people are sensitive to light and prefer darker or brighter environments. If you can install dimmer switches, your client can adjust the light level in the room, though a dimmer switch can make some kinds of lightbulbs buzz louder. If dimmer switches are not an option, have different lighting sources in your office so that your client can adjust the overall lighting level by switching different lamps on or off. If your office has windows, install curtains so that your client can decide how much (if any) natural light they are comfortable with, or so they can let more light in if they need to turn off the lightbulbs due to noise.

A Variety of Seating Options

If you see families or couples as part of your practice, you likely have multiple seating options in your office. If you only have two seats, though, or if you have a matching set with the same fabric, texture, and firmness, you limit your options for comfortable seating. It is okay to coordinate your space, but clients with sensory sensitivities might prefer softer or firmer seating, the option to put their feet up, or a seat with space to move or stim. Having a variety of seating lets your client make themselves comfortable. Even if you are not able to purchase or fit additional seating in your office, consider providing smaller accessories that will allow clients to customize their seat, such as cushions and blankets that can be placed on the floor or over a chair to provide a different texture or degree of firmness.

Neutral Colors and Images

When I was an intern, my supervisor purchased a large, brightly colored abstract painting for the office. The painting featured many small circles, which some clients reported triggered trypophobia (aversion to clusters of small holes or bumps). Some requested to meet in a different room because they found the painting so unsettling. While bare, blank walls can make your office feel sterile or unwelcoming, neutral or cool colors and soothing imagery can make the space more comfortable to clients who have visual sensory sensitivities. If this is not up to you, you can try to arrange seating so that clients can have their back to any pictures they dislike.

Space to Move

Many autistic people get uncomfortable if they have to sit still for an extended period of time, so having space to move around, sit on the floor, or fidget can help them feel more comfortable and unmask during their sessions with you.

Sensory Items

There are many different sensory items that can make autistic clients feel comfortable or encourage them to stim if they want to during their sessions with you. The following list is by no means exhaustive, as new sensory items come out all the time, and you might not be able to provide every single item on this list. Again, this is okay! Having a few items can at least give clients the chance to try out sensory items they might want to purchase and shows them that you are neurodiversity-affirming. Sensory items you might have in your office include:

1. **Balance board:** This is a small board that you stand on. It requires focus, attention, and muscle control to remain balanced on the board. This can help clients with kinetic sensory needs.

2. **Fidget items:** When most people think of fidget items, they imagine fidget spinners, which became popular a few years ago. However, this can also include monkey noodles (bits of rubber

that can stretch), flip chains (keychains that can be flipped around), infinity cubes (cubes that unfold or fold into themselves infinitely), marble fidgets (marbles inside of a small mesh tube), fidget cubes, squeeze toys, maze toys, and puzzle balls. They are also good for clients with kinetic sensory needs.

3. **Kinetic sand:** Kinetic sand is a type of play sand that holds its shape and can be sculpted but also crumbles. It is soft and comes in many colors, and it is helpful to clients with tactile sensory needs.

4. **Liquid motion bubbler:** Bubblers are similar to an hourglass, containing liquid (or sometimes sand) that can be different colors. When flipped over, the liquid travels up or down in a pattern that is interesting to watch. Liquid motion bubblers can help those with visual sensory needs.

5. **Music box:** For clients with auditory sensory needs, a music box (or simply playing music through any means) can be soothing.

6. **Orbeez:** These are tiny gel beads that grow up to one hundred times their size when put in water. Clients can put their hands in a bucket of Orbeez for tactile sensory needs.

7. **Putty:** This can include thinking putty, Play-Doh, silly putty, or another kind of putty or clay. Putty is good for clients with tactile sensory needs, and it can come in fun colors that are visually pleasing as well.

8. **Rain stick:** A rain stick is a musical instrument, often made from a dried cactus, filled with small rocks that make a noise like rain when you shake it or turn it over. Some rain sticks are several feet long, but you can also find small ones. Egg shakers make similar sounds. These are great for clients with auditory sensory needs.

9. **Sequin pillow:** A sequin pillow has sequins sewn on one side that flip back and forth when brushed with your hand. Often the sequins have a different color on either side, or they form a pattern or image when flipped one way. Sequin pillows offer both visual and tactile sensory experiences.

10. **Slime:** There are many different types of slime, and you can make your own with clients if you have the space and resources. It can be great for clients with tactile needs.

11. **Soft blanket:** Clients with tactile needs may benefit from the option to cover themselves with a soft blanket in your office. Some clients feel safer if they can cover their face when they are uncomfortable.

12. **Squishies:** These soft, squishy toys, which are often shaped like animals or food, can be very pleasing for clients with tactile needs to squish or hold.

13. **Stim jewelry:** There are many different types of jewelry that allow the wearer to stim or fidget, and you can provide a couple of options for clients to try out or use in their sessions. This can include spinning rings, beaded rings, and spinning necklaces. They are good for kinetic and visual sensory needs.

14. **Stress balls:** Most people have used a stress ball at some point. Clients who need to engage their muscles can benefit from squeezing a stress ball.

15. **Stuffed animals:** Stuffed animals are great comfort items for emotion work, especially for those working through childhood issues. They can also be visually pleasing and meet tactile sensory needs.

16. **Textured balls:** Balls with different textures on the outside are similar to stress balls, with the textures meeting tactile needs.

17. **Tops:** Moving, spinning items can be visually pleasing while meeting kinetic needs. Some tops make noise when spun, adding an auditory component.

18. **Under-desk bike:** Small, stationary bikes let you pedal and move while seated, which can help clients with kinetic sensory needs move around while staying engaged in their session.

19. **Weighted blanket:** Weighted blankets come in many sizes, and it might help clients with pressure sensory needs to have the option to drape a small weighted blanket over their lap while they meet with you.

20. **Wiggle seat:** Wiggle seats, also known as wobble cushions, are flat, inflated seats that allow you to wiggle back and forth while remaining seated. They often have small, plastic spikes that can provide pressure or tactile sensations.

21. **Yoga ball:** Yoga balls are large, inflated balls that can be used for exercise, and some people use them in place of a desk chair, as they can help you build core strength. They are a good tool for clients with kinetic sensory needs.

Chewelry (jewelry made from silicone, designed to be chewed on) is another popular sensory item for many autistic people, but for sanitary reasons you may not choose to keep them in your office for various clients to use. You can encourage clients to bring their own chewelry if they have a need to chew, or provide gum for this purpose.

If you use kinetic sand, putty, slime, Orbeez, or other items that may spill or make a mess, make sure that you have sufficient time between sessions for any necessary cleanup. If this is not an option, it may be better to limit your sensory items to ensure that you can maintain your space appropriately. Remember also that some of these items need to be replaced regularly for sanitary reasons or because they wear out.

Communicate with Your Client

It does not matter how adaptable and sensory-friendly your office is if your clients are not aware that they have the option to make adjustments. Since many autistic people have been taught to ignore their needs to avoid inconveniencing the people around them, they may not automatically assume that they have the option to make modifications. Additionally, they might have been reprimanded or punished in the past for trying to meet their sensory needs. For these reasons, the most important part of having a sensory-friendly office is making sure that your client knows what their options are to modify the space for their comfort.

At the start of treatment, let your client know they have control over the space. Tell them they are allowed to choose their seat, adjust the lighting, or use sensory items without asking permission or without waiting to be invited each time. It might take a while for them to feel fully comfortable engaging in the sensory space, and clients who are still learning to unmask may not even know what their sensory needs are, but opening this conversation early lets clients know that you are affirming and there to help them get their needs met.

Most therapists do not have the funds to simply purchase anything a client requests, but if you are able, take your clients' needs into account when it is time to purchase new supplies for your office. Let them know also that they can bring their own sensory items to their sessions to make the space more comfortable, like a specific fidget item, chewelry, or a stuffed animal.

Creating a sensory-friendly office space and communicating your commitment to meeting your client's sensory needs is part of being a neurodiversity-affirming therapist. It shows your autistic clients that their needs matter, even if they are not yet sure what those needs are. It shows that they can safely unmask with you and do not have to fear judgment or ridicule, which they may have experienced in the past. Finally, it normalizes giving them a say in what their sessions look like, as they get control of the space in a way they might not be used to.

Sensory Experiences Guided Interview

When creating a sensory-friendly office space for your clients, it's important to keep in mind that sensory needs can be complicated. There is the notion that people are either "sensory-seeking" or "sensory-avoidant," with the former meaning that someone tends to seek out sensory experiences because those experiences create positive feelings or help them self-regulate, and the latter meaning the opposite: that the individual avoids these experiences in order to self-regulate. The technical definitions of these terms imply that people fall into one of two categories, but this is misleading. For example, an individual who is sensory-seeking for tactile experiences may be sensory-avoidant to sounds. To add further nuance, many autistic people are both sensory-seeking and sensory-avoidant to the same sensory experience. For example, someone who self-regulates or stims by listening to loud music might become escalated and overstimulated when they hear someone whistling.

In order to determine what sensory interventions might be a good fit for your client, you must gather information about their individualized sensory needs. One way to do so is through the following structured sensory interview. The goal of this interview is not to assign clients a label around their sensory behaviors and needs, but to craft a narrative and gather information about the individual's needs as a big picture. I also encourage you to follow up on the interview prompts with open-ended questions, as this will sometimes yield new answers and provide you with sensory considerations that were not gleaned from the original interview. This is what happens when you see each client as a unique individual rather than a combination of symptoms to be labeled.

Additionally, this interview helps the client build insight into any sensory needs they have learned to ignore or suppress. Since many autistic people were told at an early age that their sensory needs were invalid or incorrect, or that they were being "dramatic," they might have learned to discredit their experiences or suppress their needs. By unlearning that suppression, they can begin to get their needs met again.

It is important to understand that clients often ignore their own needs for adaptive coping reasons. Although this is unhealthy in the long term, it might be necessary to suppress a need if the client knows it will not be met anyway. Learning to honor and express these needs again is part of unmasking. As a client works to recognize their needs, they might find that they have opened floodgates, causing the needs to feel big and urgent. This is expected and okay, though it can be unpleasant. Prior to embarking on a journey of unmasking, make sure the client (and, if applicable, their guardian or caretaker) is aware of this process so that they can take steps to be emotionally and physically safe as they unmask.

In addition, as an individual unmasks and learns to honor their needs, they may appear "more autistic" as they embrace themselves and begin expressing themselves authentically. When clients feel safe to express themselves authentically, you are doing your job as a therapist. However, misinformation about autism "treatment" and stigma around visibly autistic traits might cause caretakers, teachers, and others to express concern that therapy is not working or is making the client "worse." Part of your duty as a professional and expert in the field is to educate others around this topic. Whenever possible, preemptive education can ensure that they understand the true goal of supporting the autistic person and help them unlearn harmful stigmatizing attitudes.

Structured Sensory Interview

Sample Script

Everyone experiences their environment differently. For autistic people, some sensory experiences are much more or much less intense than for nonautistic people. I want to learn more about how *you* respond to sensory experiences in your environment. I will ask you a series of questions about your sensory perception in general as well as about specific sensory experiences. There are no right or wrong answers, and whatever is accurate for you is correct.

Many autistic people are taught to ignore or downplay their sensory sensitivities. As a result, you might not always know your sensory needs because you haven't had the opportunity to get them met in the past. It is perfectly okay to say you do not know the answer to a question, and we can work together to help you learn to identify your needs.

For any questions that you answer yes to, please share with me as much as you are comfortable about what this looks like for you.

General Experiences

1. Do you find that you notice sensory things in a different way than those around you?

    a. If yes, do you experience these things more intensely? What types of things?

    b. Do you experience anything less intensely than others, or not notice things that others seem to notice? What types of things?

2. Have you ever expressed that you were bothered by something in your environment, and you were told that you were "exaggerating" or being "dramatic?"

    a. If yes, what was it that bothered you?

3. Do you ever have to leave a place because it is "too much"?

4. Do you ever feel like you need to recharge after being in certain places or having certain sensory experiences?

5. Do you ever experience sensations that others tell you are "impossible"—for example, being able to hear the lights?

6. Are there any sensory experiences that you really enjoy that others find unusual, like feeling a certain texture or listening to a song on repeat?

Visual Experiences

1. How do you handle visually stimulating places?

2. What level of lighting do you prefer?

3. Do you engage in visual stims?

4. What kinds of visual experiences do you enjoy?

5. What kinds of visual media do you consume?

6. Do you struggle with tracking your place when reading?

7. Do you get frequent headaches from light?

Sound Experiences

1. Are you easily startled?

2. How do you handle loud environments?

3. At what volume do you play music or television?

4. Do you make sounds when working on something, like humming, whistling, or talking yourself through the task?

5. How often do you need to ask others to be quiet?

6. Do you ever require noise-canceling headphones to manage the sound in your environment?

7. Do you ever not notice when someone is trying to get your attention?

8. What sound-based stims do you engage in?

Tactile Experiences

1. How do you respond to physical touch from others?

2. Does anyone comment on your physical touch preferences, like saying you touch others too much?

3. What is your experience of having "mess" on your hands or face?

4. Are there any hygiene tasks you struggle with because of how they feel?

5. How do you react to bug bites?

6. How do you react to paper cuts or scrapes?

7. Are you ever overly rough without intending to be?

8. What is your experience with clothing textures?

9. What is your experience with seams or tags in clothing?

10. What is your experience with food textures?

11. What is your pain tolerance?

Pressure Experiences

1. What is your experience with heavy or weighted blankets?

2. What is your experience with tight hugs?

3. How tight do you prefer your clothes to be?

4. Do you squeeze or press on parts of your body?

5. Do you grind your teeth or clench your jaw?

6. Do you bite or chew on things?

7. When writing, how hard do you press?

Smell Experiences

1. Do you notice smells that others don't notice?

2. What kinds of smells do you like?

3. What kinds of smells do you dislike?

4. Do you enjoy sniffing things that others do not think have a strong smell?

5. Do you ever have to leave a place due to the smell?

6. Do you get headaches due to smell?

Taste Experiences

1. What kinds of foods do you prefer, and what do you enjoy about them?
2. Do you ever lick or put things in your mouth that are not food?
3. Do you ever eat things that are not food?
4. Do you prefer a limited range of foods?
5. Are there any foods you cannot eat?

Internal Experiences

1. How quickly do you notice thirst or hunger?
2. How quickly do you notice that you need to use the bathroom?
3. Do you notice when you are getting physically sick?
4. How easily do you fall asleep?
5. How often do you wake up during the night?
6. Do you experience physical sensations, like aches, frequently?

Movement Experiences

1. How do you handle it when you need to sit still for long periods of time?
2. When seated, how much do you move?
3. When not seated, how much do you move?
4. How do you handle activities where your feet have to leave the ground?
5. How do you feel about escalators?
6. How do you feel about roller coasters and other amusement park rides?
7. How often do you get motion sick?
8. What do your movement-based stims look like?

Educating Clients: Frequently Asked Questions

When an individual realizes they are (or may be) autistic, they often have a lot of questions. If they seek an evaluation for a medical diagnosis of autism, they have even more questions about autism, supportive services, and resources. This is also true for parents of children who have received an autism diagnosis. In fact, over 75 percent of autistic people and their caregivers believe that autism is misunderstood by the general public, and this perception has not improved significantly in the past five years (Bonnello, 2022).

Unfortunately, there exists a wealth of harmful and inaccurate information, especially for parents of autistic children. Certain organizations continue to perpetuate the idea that autism is a problem to be fixed rather than a neurotype to be supported. Autistic adults who experienced harm in childhood as a result of abusive "therapies" and treatment practices are rightfully and understandably angry about their experience. These individuals have the right to express that anger. When parents or guardians of autistic children interact with autistic adults, they may interpret the autistic adults' anger and trauma resulting from harm caused by the system as hostility toward the parent.

Neurodiversity-affirming diagnosticians are in a unique position. There is typically some preexisting level of trust and rapport with the parent or guardian, and in our professional role we have an air of authority. We have the opportunity to instill the importance of neurodiversity-affirming care, treatment, and support, and we can educate parents about the risks of care that is not affirming, even if that method of treatment promises "results" that they find tempting. Remember that parents may feel scared, anxious, defensive, or many other emotions in relation to their child's autism diagnosis. Feelings are valid even when they are based on misinformation or are unhelpful, and it is your job to meet the parents where they are and support them in creating an affirming environment for their autistic loved one. You can address their defensiveness without giving in to harmful myths about autism.

The following section contains scripts you can use as a starting point for answering frequently asked questions by autistic people and their parents or guardians. While these scripts focus on what you can say to parents as the provider, remember to also listen. People need to feel heard, and if parents or guardians feel that you are speaking over them, they are unlikely to listen to what you have to say. You can take time to listen to their concerns and let them know that you hear what they are saying, and then provide educational information that helps them.

Since no question-and-answer section could encompass every possible issue that could come up, remember that this guide is only a starting point. Always tailor your responses to the unique situation and with the client's individualized needs, values, and situation in mind. Have other resources available for when you encounter a question you have not previously answered, and remember that it is appropriate to say "I don't know" when that is the truth. You can gather more information to pass along to the client later; this is always preferable to sharing incorrect or harmful information.

The resource list at the end of this book can provide answers that might not be answered here, and new resources emerge all the time. If an autistic person or their parent or guardian asks what books they should read or what sources they should turn to as they educate themselves, you can use that guide to share additional information. When maintaining your library, remember to center autistic voices and firsthand experiences from many different members of the autistic community.

Should I Tell My Child They Are Autistic?

Many parents choose not to tell their child about their autism diagnosis for a variety of reasons. Some parents state that they do not want their child to "use their autism as an excuse," which is of course a harmful attitude that you need to address with the guardian. Others have a strong emotional reaction to their child's diagnosis and do not want to give their child bad news. While you do not want to fall into the trap of toxic positivity, you want to address the parent's concerns about what it means to have an autistic child, honoring both the difficulties the child may face and the strengths they may have as a result of being autistic. If the parent tells their child about their autism diagnosis, presenting it as something horrible, this can harm the child's self-esteem and sense of identity. If a parent has this hesitation about disclosing the diagnosis, it may be beneficial to work with them and educate them before the disclosure to ensure the child receives accurate and affirming information about their diagnosis.

Regardless of age, a person who has been evaluated for and diagnosed as autistic has a right to that information about themselves. Even if they are a child when they receive their diagnosis, they are still a human being with autonomy. This is not to mention that autistic children become autistic adults who have the right to request their medical records. When an adult sees that their parents knew they were autistic for years and did not share this information, they may rightfully feel deceived, hurt, and angry. Honesty is key in preserving the parent-child relationship.

Gaining knowledge about one's neurotype is also beneficial to that individual. According to Bonnello (2022), approximately 88 percent of autistic people knew that they were different from an early age even if they did not have the word *autism* to describe their experience. Additionally, 89 percent indicated that learning that they were autistic positively impacted them.

The following script is intended to help you address a parent's concern about whether or not to disclose a child's autism diagnosis to that child. Of course, you will need to tweak the wording based on individual needs, values, and questions, but you can use this as a starting point to get around a parent's defensiveness and to provide affirming, accurate education.

Sample Script

I'm hearing that you're not sure about telling your child that they are autistic. You're concerned about how they will react to that information, and you are still processing your own feelings about parenting an autistic child. Of course, that was a big piece of information to take in, and it's okay to have feelings about it. You might feel like you're grieving the nonautistic child that you do not have, but remember that your autistic child is here, alive, and relying on you to love them and care for them. They are wonderful in their own way, and you get to know them on a new level now.

Autism is a neurotype, which means that the way your child perceives and interacts with the world around them, experiences their environment, thinks, and feels are fundamentally different from how a nonautistic person experiences those things. Autistic people have struggles, some of which come from existing in a world that holds them to nonautistic expectations, sometimes arbitrarily. They may also be disabled as a result of their autism regardless of their environment and accommodations. *Disabled* is not a bad word, and your child's life is worthwhile regardless of their disability status.

You might worry about your child if their autism or their disability makes life harder for them. You love your child, and you want them to have the best life possible. That is valid. At the same time, their disability does not make them any less wonderful or any less your child.

When it comes to talking to your child about autism and their diagnosis, at the end of the day, it is a fact about them, their brain, and their life. They have a right to accurate information about themselves, which includes knowing that they are autistic. We can make a plan to share this information with them and answer any questions they have, and you can take time to emotionally prepare and process your own feelings before telling them. At the same time, you don't want to put it off for too long—eventually, your child will have the right to request their medical records, and if they learn that you kept this from them, they might not trust you about other things in the future.

A child might not be old enough to fully understand their needs, but fortunately autistic adults can tell us about their experiences, and we can use that information to inform how we care for autistic children now. Most autistic adults say that they knew they were different from an early age, long before they discovered they were autistic. That tells us that your child probably already has a feeling that they are not like their nonautistic peers and just lack the language to express that. They might think they are "weird" or "bad," and understanding that they are autistic could help them understand their differences and be kinder to themselves.

Autistic adults also say that finding out about their autism diagnosis had a positive impact on them—it allowed them to realize what their needs are, to learn how to communicate those needs in a way that adults around them can understand, and to get those needs met in a healthy way. If your child doesn't accurately understand their needs or how to get those needs met, they might turn to harmful or dangerous behaviors. You want them to have the tools to make the best, safest choices for themselves, and knowing they are autistic is a big part of that.

How Should I Tell My Child They Are Autistic?

Even parents who fully understand the importance of sharing the diagnosis with their autistic child might not know where to start when it comes to talking to their child about their diagnosis. As with most things, there is no one "right" way to tell a child that they are autistic. (Though there are certainly wrong ways to do this!) The specific wording and the nature of the disclosure will depend on the family's values and cultural norms as well as the parent's preferences. While you cannot simply tell the family what the best route is for them, you can help them come to their own decision and encourage them to share the diagnosis with the child in an affirming way, without harming the child's self-esteem or communicating to them that they are bad, wrong, or broken. You can use the following script to guide the parent or guardian in determining the method that is best for them.

Sample Script

It can be hard to decide the best way to share your child's autism diagnosis with them. The good and bad news is that there isn't one right answer, which means you get to decide what is best for your family, but it also means that I can't just tell you what to do. We can work together to figure out the best way for your child to learn about their diagnosis. I have some questions that can help us determine what will work best for your family:

1. How are you currently feeling about your child's autism diagnosis?

2. What questions do you still have about your child's autism diagnosis?

3. What does your child know about the evaluation they completed?

4. What does your child know about autism?

5. What worries do you have about telling your child that they are autistic?

6. Do you feel it would be helpful for me to be there and help you talk to your child about their diagnosis?

7. What do you feel is the most important thing for you to tell your child during this conversation?

8. What are your family's next steps post-diagnosis? Your child should know this too.

Who Else Should We (or I) Tell?

This question may come from a parent or guardian of an autistic child or from an autistic person learning about their diagnosis. While being autistic is not shameful or bad, stigma still exists around the diagnosis. Some people are rightfully hesitant to share the information openly, and others are rightfully excited to tell everyone. Once again, each individual is making the right choice for themselves, and your role as a neurodiversity-affirming provider is to help them figure out what this means for them.

The following section includes two scripts, one for parents or guardians and one for autistic adults, to help guide the discussion in deciding whether or not to disclose the autism diagnosis. Although the first script talks directly to the parent or guardian—since this is the person who makes legal decisions about accommodations—the autistic child has a right to be part of this conversation as well.

Sample Script for Parents or Guardians

You are trying to figure out who else to share your child's autism diagnosis with. This can be a hard decision because of stigma, and you don't always know how someone will react until after you tell them. If you aren't sure about disclosing, it is okay to wait! You can't put the genie back in the bottle, and once someone knows your child is autistic, they will never stop having that information.

It might be helpful for family members and loved ones to know that your child is autistic because it can help them understand when your child has a hard time, becomes overstimulated, or needs support. At the same time, if you know there are people with strong prejudices in your family, you might decide it is not safe to share that information with them.

If your child is having a hard time at school, they qualify for academic accommodations, including an individual education plan (IEP) or 504 plan, because they are autistic. Of course, in order to set this up, the school's education planning committee needs to know what they are accommodating. It is possible that your child's teacher will treat them differently once they know your child is autistic. This isn't acceptable or appropriate, but it happens. If your child is doing well at school, you might decide that the school doesn't need to know their diagnosis. If your child has another diagnosis in addition to autism, you might choose to disclose that diagnosis but not the autism diagnosis. For example, ADHD has many similar accommodations to autism.

Let's talk through some questions to help us decide who gets to know that your child is autistic:

1. How is your child doing in school? Are they struggling or excelling?

2. Are there any settings in which your child has a particularly hard time?

3. Does the person you're considering disclosing the diagnosis to know any other autistic people, as far as you are aware?

4. How does your child feel about disclosing their autism diagnosis?

Sample Script for Autistic Adults

Now that you know you're autistic, it is up to you what you want to do with this information. People have different feelings about sharing that they are autistic, and all of those feelings are valid. On the one hand, there is nothing wrong or shameful about being autistic, and you might even feel excited to know yourself better. You might want to tell everyone! And it's your right to do that if you so choose.

On the other hand, there is stigma around autism. People who know you're autistic might treat you differently and discriminate against you. This is not okay, but it does happen. The fact that you are autistic is a private piece of information about you, and you have the right to keep that information private. Even if you aren't worried about discrimination, the fact that you're autistic is no one's business unless you choose to disclose, and if you choose not to disclose for your own safety, that's valid. It is your information, and you get to decide how private that information is.

Here are some questions we can talk through to help you decide how you want to proceed:

1. How do you feel about telling people that you are autistic?

2. How do you feel about keeping your autism diagnosis to yourself?

3. What concerns do you have about telling people you are autistic?

4. What concerns do you have about not telling people you are autistic?

I Already Enrolled My Child in ABA—Am I Terrible?

As previously noted in this book, many autistic people who experienced ABA found the experience abusive or traumatic. Some ABA practitioners acknowledge the harm that ABA has done in the past but maintain that the practice has changed and is no longer abusive. According to Bonnello (2022), 73 percent of autistic adults who received "old ABA" disagree with the assertion that ABA is beneficial to autistic children, while 63 percent who experienced "new ABA" still do not support its use. While roughly 14 percent were in favor of "new ABA," the majority of autistic people continue to indicate that ABA is not a beneficial treatment for autistic people.

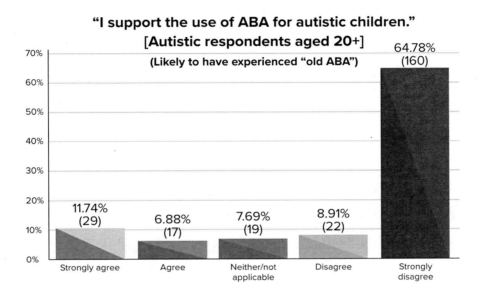

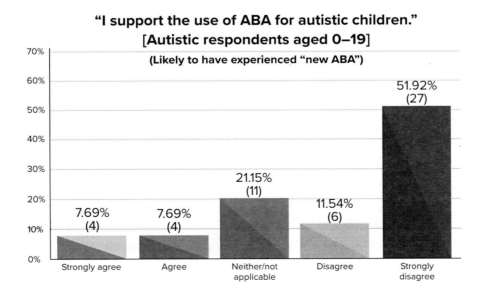

From *Results and Analysis of the Autistic Not Weird 2022 Autism Survey* (https://autisticnotweird.com/autismsurvey).
Copyright © 2022 by Chris Bonnello. Reprinted with permission.

Practitioners who have used ABA in the past or continue to use it might resist the idea that they could have done something harmful. Because of this cognitive dissonance, practitioners are likely to "dig in" and further insist that they have not done anything wrong. Parents who have enrolled their child in ABA might feel the same way. They want what is best for their child, a professional told them that ABA was best, and they followed that recommendation. No parent wants to hear that a decision they made may have harmed their child, so they may also be inclined to insist that the treatment they chose was not harmful.

Additionally, there is a lot of pressure to parent the "right" way. Although trends have shifted, many people continue to carry the attitude that parents should extract compliance by any means necessary. If someone's measure of success is whether or not a child is compliant, ABA is effective in getting children to obey. Since many autistic people who underwent ABA were forced to mask, it can look like this treatment was successful in making a child "less autistic."

Autistic children who struggle to communicate their needs (or who have their needs ignored) often engage in more extreme behaviors in order to get their needs met. They might become aggressive, harm themselves, damage property, or run away. When a parent does not understand why these behaviors are happening, they may be tempted to pursue the "treatment" option that promises to keep their child physically safe. While a neurodiversity-affirming provider understands the harms that can occur with ABA, it's also crucial to recognize that most parents are trying their best with the information available to them at the time. Your job is to help them recognize that they can do better in the future.

When talking to parents about ABA, consider cultural and identity factors that may contribute to a parent's thought process and decision-making around ABA. For example, many Black parents are rightfully concerned about dangers their children might face in interactions with law enforcement. For these parents, a treatment protocol that promises compliance might seem like a viable option for helping their child remain safe in these situations. Black parents have been berated in autistic spaces for this choice, when the underlying issue here is that parents should not have to worry that their child will die because they were deemed "dangerous" when having a meltdown in public.

This is an essential topic when having conversations with parents and guardians about parenting support and resources. As a White person, it is not my place to speak to the experience of Black autistic people and their loved ones, so I highly encourage you to follow Black autistic voices and to look at the resources created by and for the Black autistic community that are listed at the end of this book. We must address the oppressive systems that put parents in a position to make these choices.

In the following script, you'll find guidance to help parents or guardians navigate the feelings they may have about enrolling their child in ABA. Note that this script includes some self-disclosure as an example of how a clinician might continue to grow. Use your discretion in deciding whether to include a personal example with your own clients.

Sample Script

Parenting is hard. There's no manual, and a lot of traditional parenting advice assumes children are neurotypical. You've been confused and frustrated, and you have made decisions based on inaccurate or limited information. I believe you when you tell me that you want what is best for your child and that you made treatment decisions based on what professionals told you was best.

We are always learning and growing. When we learn that something we did in the past was harmful, it is okay to accept this, make amends, and grow. My graduate program didn't teach neurodiversity-affirming care and taught me some inaccurate information about autism. Fortunately, as I have continued to grow as a professional, I have learned to be better and have adjusted my practice based on that new information. You are doing the same thing now as you learn more about the most beneficial way to get your child's needs met and adjust your approach based on new information.

You might have feelings of guilt or regret, but remember that you were doing your best with the information you had at the time. Now that you have new information, the best thing you can do for your child is change your approach in light of that information.

Why Should We Take a Neurodiversity-Affirming Approach to Treatment?

As noted in the previous section, parents might be tempted to pursue a nonaffirming approach to treatment because they prioritize compliance or obedience. We often confuse well-behaved children for well-adjusted children, when in fact a child who behaves *too* well might actually be highly anxious. Personal beliefs about children's behavior, judgment from others, and intergenerational patterns might contribute to a parent's desire to focus on behavior and compliance rather than well-being. The following script can help parents understand how an affirming approach benefits their child and explore their own beliefs and priorities about treatment.

Sample Script

As a parent, you're constantly getting conflicting messages about what you "should" do or how to make the "right" choice for your child. That can be confusing and scary. While I can't tell you what is best for your family, I can give you information about your options. As a mental health provider, my priority is to make sure that your child is safe, both physically and emotionally, which is why I have concerns about treatment that is not affirming. If a treatment approach has been shown to cause trauma, I cannot ethically endorse that approach because even if it leads to the behavior you want to see from your child, it is hurting them psychologically.

You might find yourself saying, "When I was a child, I never would have acted that way in front of my parents!" That may be true, but I invite you to consider, *why* wouldn't you have acted that way in front of your parents? What did you think might happen if you let your parents see you struggling like that? What did you think they would do, and do you want your child to think you will do the same thing to them?

While a neurodiversity-affirming approach to supporting your child might not lead to immediate behavior changes, it can help them become well-adjusted emotionally and learn to recognize and honor their needs. We can work together to find a way for your child to communicate those needs in a way that you can understand. This will help their mental health in the long term.

Will My Child Be Able to Live Independently?

Parents want their child to live their best life and to become a "functional adult," which many define as being able to live on their own. For some autistic people, this might not be an appropriate and safe decision. This does not mean they have any less value or worth as people, but the issue of independent living may still be a valid concern that parents have. There may also be an underlying worry about what will happen to the child as the parents grow older. Parents typically do not expect to outlive their children, and if a child has high support needs, the parent might rightfully worry about what will happen to the child when the parent dies or is no longer able to care for them.

This is not a problem with an easy solution, and the parent might need to continue to seek supportive services for their child over time. They might need a plan in place that describes what will happen if they are suddenly unable to provide care and support to their child. The script that follows is merely a starting point for this conversation to address the parent's immediate worries.

Sample Script

It makes complete sense that you would worry about your child's well-being and want them to have the best life possible! Some autistic people live fully independently, and some require various levels of support. You might be worried about how your child will get that support as they get older.

We don't know with certainty what anyone's future will hold. If your child has other diagnoses, they might have added support needs related to those conditions. Remember that your child's support needs don't make them any less worthy or any less wonderful of a human. If you are worried about who will care for your child if or when you are unable to, we can talk about what resources and supports they qualify for based on their disability status. We can put a plan in place to make sure that your child has the support they need no matter what.

How Can I Know Whether a Therapy Is Affirming?

Neurodiversity-affirming is a relatively new term in the clinical space. While the autistic community has vocalized the need for affirming care for a long time, many people do not understand what it means to be affirming or why it is important. Since autistic people and their guardians might not be familiar with this term or the underlying philosophy and want to know what to look for, use this script to help them understand the difference between affirming and nonaffirming therapies.

Sample Script

Neurodiversity-affirming care acknowledges that neurodivergence is not a bad thing and that neurodiversity is a net positive in the world. It includes an awareness of the unique strengths that a neurodivergent person might have, while also honoring that neurodivergence can be disabling. It's not bad or wrong to be disabled, and we do not want to overlook the challenges that can come with neurodivergence.

When therapy is neurodiversity-affirming for an autistic person, it means that the therapist acknowledges that autism is not a problem to be solved and that the autistic person is not broken or in need of being fixed. The therapist works to help the autistic person understand their brain and their needs, and they help the autistic person learn strategies to get their needs met in a healthy way.

If a therapist wants to help their client become "less autistic," they are not affirming. If a therapist wants their client to stop stimming because it is "disruptive" or otherwise a problem, they are not affirming. If a therapist focuses their goals on making the autistic person convenient for the people around them, they are not affirming. Affirming care centers the autistic client's needs and finds creative, safe, and healthy ways to get those needs met.

You can ask providers if they are mindful of making their therapy neurodiversity-affirming. You can ask if they understand what this means and how they know they are being affirming. Some therapist directories even let you filter for therapists who describe themselves as neurodiversity-affirming.

Are You Sure I Am (or My Child Is) Autistic?

Autistic "impostor syndrome" is common, even in those who have had an extensive evaluation confirming that they are autistic. What's more, barriers to assessment and diagnosis prevent many from getting an official diagnosis, which has led to people in the autistic community embracing self-identification or self-diagnosis. From a neurodiversity-affirming standpoint, it is essential to recognize that if a client benefits from support systems that help autistic people, they should have access to those supports even if they have not been tested for autism.

In the *DSM-5-TR*, one of the symptoms or traits of autism is the presence of restricted and repetitive behaviors, interests, or activities, which can manifest as a strong need for certainty before accepting information as true. This can mean that some autistic people will question whether they are autistic. Autistic traits can manifest in infinite different ways, and just like nonautistics, autistic people are unique individuals. For some, this fuels the fear that they are not "really autistic" because some of the traits or behaviors that other autistic people exhibit are not personally relatable to them.

Since this question can take many different forms, there is not a sample script you can follow when navigating this concern with clients. However, you can explore what things they have noticed that have them questioning their autism. If you are the provider who diagnosed them, you can review the measures that you used with the client and talk about how mental health professionals use those measures to identify autism. Normalize this question and let the client know that many autistic people ask the same thing.

What Level Do I (or Does My Child) Have? Am I (or Are They) High or Low Functioning?

When the American Psychiatric Association changed the designation of PDD-NOS, autism, and Asperger's syndrome to the umbrella of autism spectrum disorder, it was decided that they still needed a designation to reflect how "high functioning" or "low functioning" an individual is, which is where the *DSM*'s current level system originated.

The level system has received pushback from the autistic community because it frames an autistic person's traits in light of how they impact the people around them, rather than the autistic person's well-being. It also focuses on the autistic person's ability to work, or function under capitalism, which is not the bar for mental well-being. This is not to mention that an autistic person experiencing burnout might function on a different level than they previously did, and an autistic person who receives needed support might function differently as well. Additionally, an individual might meet the criteria for different levels when it comes to different traits; for example, someone whose sensory sensitivities are level 2 might have level 3 or level 1 social traits.

Some neurodiversity-affirming providers choose not to use levels because of these problems with the system. Others utilize the system with an awareness of its flaws because a level designation is sometimes necessary to access needed services. Each provider must decide what is most appropriate for them in their practice. If you use the level system, you can explain it to the client in the context of the traits you observe and how those fit into the system. If you choose not to use the level system, here is a script for explaining that reasoning to the autistic person or their guardian, as appropriate.

Sample Script

The *DSM*—which is the main diagnostic manual for mental health and brain-related conditions used in the United States—uses a level system to designate how much support an autistic person needs. Many providers take issue with this system because it focuses on how "severe" the person's autism is and how much they inconvenience the people around them, rather than the autistic person's needs. Some providers still use the level system and find it helpful because it can help clients get access to supportive services that they might benefit from.

Your level can be inconsistent, as you might need no help at all in one area but a lot of help in another. Your level can also fluctuate with burnout and other factors. If you learn to unmask more, you might find that you seem to have more needs because you've just begun to acknowledge them. The needs were always there, but you did not recognize them before. Therefore, instead of focusing on your level, it can be more accurate to think about what your exact needs are and what supports have benefited you. This is an ongoing discussion because your needs may change over time and you might realize needs you had not previously honored.

What Other Things Should We Test For?

Autistic people are more likely than nonautistic people to have a significant number of medical conditions, mental health diagnoses, and other neurodivergences. While none of these comorbidities are guaranteed just because someone is autistic, certain symptoms might indicate that further testing would be beneficial. The testing recommendations should be personalized based on the individual's symptoms, as it can be easy to overwhelm someone with a huge number of possible conditions. Of course, always stay up to date on research because new information becomes available all the time. This list is simply a starting point for determining what recommendations you can make.

Medical Diagnoses

- **Autoimmune disorders:** Conditions in which the body's immune system is unable to distinguish safe and dangerous cells, and the immune system may attack the body.

- **Chronic fatigue syndrome (CFS):** A medical condition consisting of excessive fatigue, brain fog, sleep issues, and difficulty with movement activities.

- **Connective tissue disorders:** Different disorders that occur when the connective tissue within the body becomes inflamed, including Ehlers-Danlos Syndrome (EDS), which is particularly common in autistic individuals.

- **Endometriosis:** A condition that occurs when cells similar to those of the uterine lining grow outside of the uterus.

- **Fibromyalgia:** A chronic pain disorder that causes sleep problems, fatigue, and physical pain.

- **Gastritis:** Inflammation in the stomach lining.

- **Irritable bowel syndrome (IBS):** A group of gastrointestinal symptoms, including diarrhea, constipation, and abdominal pain.

- **Mast cell activation syndrome (MCAS):** A condition that occurs when the body issues an allergic reaction—including hives, breathing problems, and swelling—without a specific allergen trigger.

- **Migraines:** Severe headaches that can interfere with vision, sensitivity, and functioning.

- **Osteoporosis:** A bone disease caused by reduced bone density, which can lead to fractures and reduced bone strength.

- **Postural orthostatic tachycardia syndrome (POTS):** An orthostatic intolerance disorder where the individual's blood returns to their heart after standing up, which can cause dizziness and fainting.

- **Sinus problems:** Difficulty with sinus drainage and frequent sinus infections.

- **Sleep apnea:** A sleep disorder in which breathing pauses or gets very shallow during sleep.

- **Temperature sensitivity:** A propensity to overheat or experience heat stroke more easily.

- **Tuberous sclerosis:** A genetic disease in which benign tumors grow in and on various organs in the body.

- **Vision problems:** A propensity toward vision problems, such as strabismus (i.e., crossed eyes), that require corrective lenses.

Psychological Diagnoses

- **Anxiety:** Mental health conditions that involve disproportionate fear, nervousness, or worry about threats, whether the threats are real or hypothetical.

- **ADHD:** A neurodevelopmental disorder marked by issues with inattention and/or hyperactivity and impulsivity.

- **Depression:** Clinically significant, persistent mood symptoms that interfere with functioning, sleep, and motivation.

- **Eating disorders:** Due to sensory issues or medical problems related to food sensitivities, autistic people are more likely than nonautistic people to develop eating disorders, including avoidant/restrictive food intake disorder (ARFID).

- **Learning disorders:** Difficulty in one or more academic areas not caused by another mental health diagnosis or lack of intelligence, including dyslexia (learning disorder in reading), dyscalculia (learning disorder in math), dysgraphia (learning disorder in writing), and others.

- **Obsessive-compulsive disorder (OCD):** OCD is marked by intrusive, disturbing thoughts in conjunction with repetitive behaviors to alleviate feelings of disturbance caused by the thoughts. Related disorders also include body-focused repetitive behaviors, such as skin picking and hair pulling. Autistic people may be misdiagnosed with OCD due to the overlap between OCD symptoms and autistic traits, or they may experience OCD or a related disorder in addition to being autistic.

- **PTSD and other trauma-related disorders:** A mental health condition that develops in response to a highly stressful or traumatic event, which is characterized by intrusive memories or flashbacks, hypervigilance, sleep disturbance, irritability, focus issues, and increased startle response. Autistic people are at higher risk for childhood abuse compared to nonautistic people, and the community reports lifelong stressors related to masking that can cause trauma symptoms.

- **Premenstrual dysphoric disorder (PMDD):** A severe form of premenstrual syndrome marked by both physical and emotional symptoms, including extreme changes in mood, anger, anxiety, depression, fatigue, physical pain, and other symptoms.

- **Substance use disorders:** Many autistic people report using substances to cope with life stressors, especially when they are unable to receive adequate and appropriate support.

- **Suicidal ideation or behavior:** Autistic people are at higher risk for suicidal ideation and behavior than nonautistic people, which can be connected to trauma or another mental health issue noted in this section.

Other

- **Alexithymia:** Inability to identify or describe the emotions you are experiencing.

- **Aphantasia:** Inability to mentally visualize images.

- **Aphasia:** Communication difficulties.

- **Atypical pain responses:** Autistic people report different pain experiences than nonautistic people, whether they experience severe pain from a seemingly minor injury or do not exhibit a pain response at all to a severe injury. Many experience more severe pain than typical in some situations and simultaneously less severe pain in others.

- **Avoidance of medical treatment:** Autistic people often avoid seeking medical treatment even when they feel they need medical attention. For some, hospitals and clinics are overstimulating, and they are unable to tolerate these environments. Others have experienced doctors dismiss their complaints or even accuse them of being dishonest about their symptoms, leading them to be less likely to seek treatment in the future.

- **Food sensitivities:** Just like autistic people are more likely than nonautistic people to experience gastrointestinal issues and various allergies, they may be more sensitive to certain foods and ingredients, even if these sensitivities do not rise to the threshold of a medical diagnosis. Autistic people may notice that they feel ill after eating certain types of food, which can lead to a limited diet.

- **Hypersomnia:** Needing more sleep than is typical.

- **Insomnia:** Difficulty falling or staying asleep.

- **Medication sensitivities or atypical medication response:** Many autistic people experience unusual side effects to medication and may feel the effects of medication more strongly than others. For example, some autistic people who take antidepressant medication report benefits with a "subclinical" dose. Others experience side effects that are not listed because they are so uncommon. Some experience the opposite of the typical, desired effect.

- **Prosopagnosia:** Inability to recognize faces.

- **Synesthesia:** A condition in which someone experiences sensory input through a different sense. Most commonly, this is described as perceiving letters, words, or numbers as colors. However, it can also be experienced as perceiving sounds or sights as smells or tastes, or through the condition of "mirror touch" (feeling touch when you see someone else being touched). Synesthesia can cause autistic people to be misdiagnosed with psychotic disorders, as screening measures might misinterpret synesthesia as hallucinations.

Some of these conditions can be caused by stroke or brain damage, but autistic people report experiencing them without a known history of brain injury at a higher rate than nonautistic people. Remember also that each autistic person is one of a kind, so none of these considerations are guaranteed for an autistic person. However, if a client has additional symptoms, this list can be a good starting point for determining what might be happening. It can also help the autistic person realize when something falls outside of what is considered "normal" and seek support for symptoms they may have been coping with despite stress or medical issues this has caused.

Is Autism Genetic?

While we do not fully understand all the interactions around genetics, there is evidence that autism is genetic. A person is more likely to be autistic if they have a parent, sibling, or other relative who is autistic. There are researchers seeking to identify which genes specifically "cause" autism, but so far this research is inconclusive, as it is likely that autism manifests as a result of the interaction of many different genes.

Although understanding people's genetic makeup can help providers find an appropriate medication for an individual or alleviate pain related to medical issues, many people seek to determine a genetic cause for autism because they are motivated to eradicate autistic people and make sure no new autistic people are born. Autism research has a long history in eugenics, and it is important to keep this in mind when discussing biological influences on neurotype with clients.

Sample Script

Genetics are unbelievably complex, but we have found that autism tends to run in families. First-degree relatives of autistic people are more likely to also be autistic than those who do not have an autistic relative. This is not a guarantee, but since we know that you are autistic, if you've noticed similar traits in your children, you might decide to have them evaluated as well. (For parents: If you notice similarities between your child's autistic traits and your own experience, or similar traits in your other children, you might decide to pursue evaluation.)

You might get invited to participate in genetics research to better understand autism. It is your right to decide whether or not to participate, but know that some of these researchers want to learn how to get rid of autistic people. Make sure you vet the companies and individuals conducting this research because you deserve to work with providers who care for you and affirm you.

Can I Request Accommodations at Work?

Many autistic adults struggle with finding and keeping employment, with approximately half having trouble finding employment and about 46 percent having trouble keeping jobs (Bonnello, 2022). The following graphs illustrate some of these difficulties.

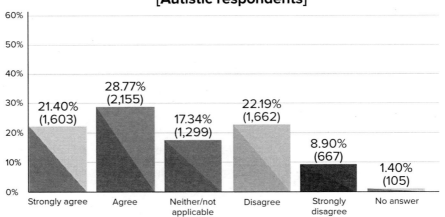

"I struggle (or have struggled) with <u>finding</u> employment."
[Autistic respondents]

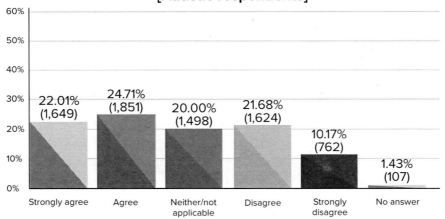

"I struggle (or have struggled) with <u>retaining</u> employment."
[Autistic respondents]

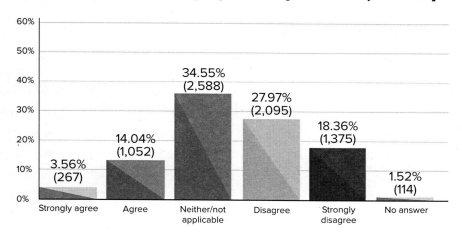

"Generally speaking, my workplace/s have done a good job of accommodating my needs." [Autistic respondents]

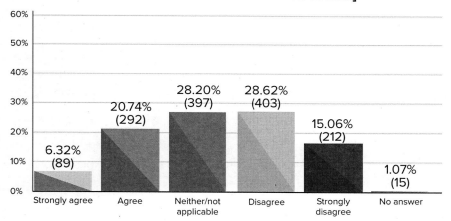

"Generally speaking, my workplace/s have done a good job of accommodating my needs." [Autistic respondents who work with autistic students/clients]

From *Results and Analysis of the Autistic Not Weird 2022 Autism Survey* (https://autisticnotweird.com/autismsurvey). Copyright © 2022 by Chris Bonnello. Reprinted with permission.

Those who have jobs or want to find work have the option to request accommodations under the Americans with Disabilities Act (ADA), which defines autism as a disability and requires that employers offer reasonable accommodations. While the ADA indicates that a person requesting accommodations only needs to provide documentation confirming the disability and do *not* have to share the specific diagnosis, schools and employers very frequently request this information anyway. Multiple lawsuits have resulted from this, and judges have historically sided with the employer, requiring that the individual disclose their diagnosis despite what the ADA says. The individual has the right to say that they do not want to share their diagnosis, but if they are open about being autistic, they might choose to share their diagnosis to streamline the process.

Unfortunately, it can be difficult to enforce the ADA, and many choose to answer the question in order to access accommodations.

Sample Script

If you need accommodations at work, you qualify for those under the ADA, as autism is classified as a disability. According to the ADA, your employer can ask for documentation confirming that you have a disability before providing accommodations. Technically they aren't allowed to ask *what* your disability is, but many ask anyway, and unfortunately case law indicates that you will likely be required to disclose if they ask. The problem with the ADA is that it's hard to enforce. If you choose to tell your employer, that might streamline your accommodation request. You have the right not to tell them, and as your provider, I'll only share the information you authorize.

I unfortunately can't guarantee they will help you and will not discriminate against you. In most states, we have something called "right to work," which means your employer can fire you for no reason. It would be illegal for them to fire you for being autistic, but if they don't disclose a reason, it could be difficult to prove to a judge that you were fired for being autistic. You have to decide for yourself what is safest and right for your own life.

Can I Request Accommodations at School?

Students with an autism diagnosis can get academic accommodations under the ADA and the Individuals with Disabilities Education Act (IDEA) regardless of their age. While this typically requires disclosing the diagnosis to the school so they can provide an appropriate IEP or 504 plan, these accommodations might be beneficial, as more than 80 percent of autistic adults report not having had a positive experience in school and 46 percent of parents and caregivers feel their child's school does not know how to support their child (Bonnello, 2022).

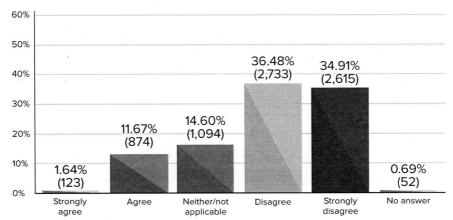

"My experience at school was positive."
[All autistic respondents]

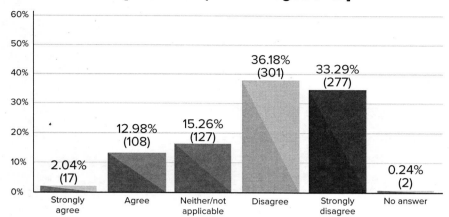

"My experience at school was positive."
[Autistic respondents aged 0–19]

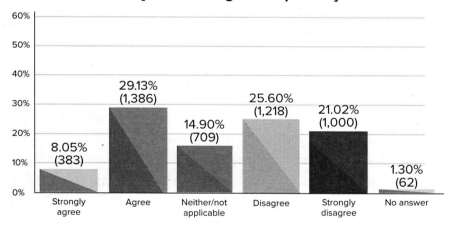

"My school knows/knew how to support my child."
[Parent/caregiver responses]

From *Results and Analysis of the Autistic Not Weird 2022 Autism Survey* (https://autisticnotweird.com/autismsurvey).
Copyright © 2022 by Chris Bonnello. Reprinted with permission.

Sample Script

You have the option to pursue academic accommodations based on an autism diagnosis, and you might decide this is a helpful route because many autistic people struggle academically and socially, with most reporting that school was not a positive experience for them. This would entail sharing the diagnosis with the school, which you have the right to do, of course. If you are concerned about teachers treating your child differently if they know about the diagnosis, you want to consider that before sharing that information.

If you do decide to seek accommodations at school, these will be individualized based on your child's needs. We can talk through the difficulties and decide what accommodations will be most helpful. Here are some questions to consider:

1. In what areas does your child struggle?
2. In what areas are they doing well?
3. What are triggers in their current school environment?
4. What helps them manage these triggers?
5. What would a supportive environment look like?
6. What needs to change for the school environment to be supportive?

What Supports Do I Need?

Disabled autistic people have varying levels of support needs. For some, this means having workplace accommodations, not working full time, or not working at all. Some struggle to manage finances without support, and some might need live-in support to address and meet their needs. If an autistic person has other disabilities unrelated to their autism, they are more likely to need more support.

Regardless of an individual's support needs, a neurodiversity-affirming approach means that you maximize independence wherever appropriate. For example, if an autistic adult struggles to manage their money, an affirming provider or case manager would work with them to teach this skill and develop a budget that works for them rather than appointing a conservator who controls all of the autistic person's money. While it may be tempting to take control of their finances "for their own good"—perhaps you believe you're protecting them from their own choices—remember that nonautistic people sometimes make poor financial choices, too, and that is their right as autonomous adults. To honor the individual's autonomy, conservatorship and full control should be a last resort.

Behaviors that would not be considered a problem in nonautistic adults are sometimes labeled as unsafe in an autistic adult, such as frivolous spending habits, inconsistent sleep patterns, or engaging in sexual activity with other adults. Consider what is needed to keep the individual physically and psychologically safe, and remember that autonomous adults sometimes make mistakes. One survey asked disabled adults what they would change about their supportive living environment, and many stated that they would like the option to choose their own bedtime (James et al., 2018). Even when a supportive living environment is necessary, this level of control over an adult is infantilizing.

Affirming care does not mean removing all supports, however. Each autistic person will have their own support needs, and you can help them figure out what services allow them to be their best without infantilizing them or taking control of their life in an inappropriate way. Autistic people are more likely to find places inaccessible compared to nonautistic people, which may cause autistic people to need support in order to function in these environments (Bonnello, 2022). For example:

- Approximately 60 percent of autistic people find schools inaccessible compared to 39 percent of nonautistic people.

- Approximately 56 percent of autistic people find healthcare services inaccessible compared to 42 percent of nonautistic people.

- About 57 percent of autistic people find public places inaccessible compared to 49 percent of nonautistic people. The survey did not inquire about what made the space accessible, but this can include being sensory-friendly and, if applicable, having dietary options that meet a variety of needs.

- About 56 percent of autistic people feel community groups (such as gatherings, concerts, or other events) are inaccessible compared to 41 percent of nonautistic people.

Many of these accessibility issues could be curbed simply by making places more accessible (e.g., having space for sensory breaks, not requiring specific dress codes that may be uncomfortable, or ensuring accessibility for those with mobility issues), though some individuals might still need support regardless of these changes. You can use the following brief script to help your autistic clients explore what supports they would benefit from.

Sample Script

Everyone has different needs, and autistic people are more likely than nonautistic people to require certain support in order to function. It's okay if you need help with certain things, and one thing we can do together is figure out what supports would benefit you. My goal is for you to be as independent as possible while still getting any help you need in order to have your best life. Tell me more about the things that give you the hardest time, and we can look into finding supportive services that will benefit you.

What Is Autistic Masking?

Many newly diagnosed autistic people ask about masking, which is a strategy autistic people use to hide behaviors and traits that make them appear outwardly autistic in an effort to present like nonautistic people. They might hide certain behaviors they normally engage in (e.g., stimming) or learn neurotypical behaviors that allow them to fit in. Not all autistic people mask, or are able to mask, and historically the ability to mask has been used as evidence that those individuals are not truly autistic. We now know that many autistic people mask, though some are unable to. All experiences are unique and valid.

Autistic people of all ages, but especially children, sometimes mask without realizing what is happening. When everyone is assumed neurotypical, and neurotypical brains are considered superior to neurodivergent brains, children unconsciously pick up on the ways that their authentic selves do not meet others' expectations. As a result, they sometimes begin masking to try to meet these expectations. They may suppress stimming behavior, force themselves to communicate in ways that are uncomfortable for them, and tolerate harmful sensory experiences rather than seeking to get their needs met. When someone masks unintentionally, they may forget how to unmask and continue masking even when they are alone. Long-term masking is harmful and can lead to burnout, so learning to unmask is a process that autistic people can find helpful. It allows them to get to know themselves better and honor their needs.

At the same time, it is not always safe to unmask. Autistic people might be bullied or mistreated for autistic behaviors they show when they unmask. If an autistic person wants or needs to mask to protect themselves, they are allowed to do so. In fact, 84 percent of autistic people feel the need to mask when spending time with nonautistic people (Bonnello, 2022). The following script can help you introduce the concept of masking to your client, especially if they are newly diagnosed as autistic and may be unfamiliar with the term.

"I feel the need to mask my personality in groups of <u>nonautistic</u> people."
[Autistic respondents]

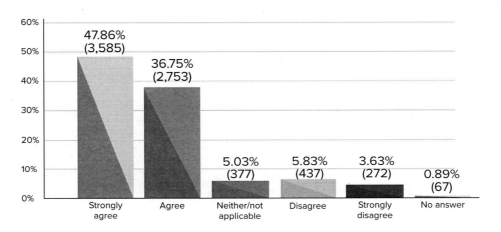

"I feel the need to mask my personality in groups of <u>autistic</u> people."
[Autistic respondents]

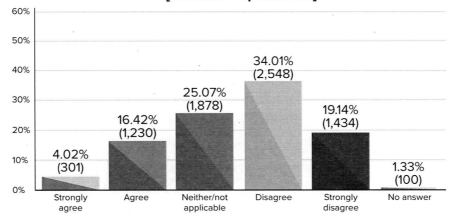

From *Results and Analysis of the Autistic Not Weird 2022 Autism Survey* (https://autisticnotweird.com/autismsurvey).
Copyright © 2022 by Chris Bonnello. Reprinted with permission.

Sample Script

Masking, which some people call camouflaging, occurs when an autistic person feels the need to change how they behave in order to present like they are not autistic. Not all autistic people mask or are able to mask, but it is possible you mask or have masked in the past. You might not even have realized it's happening because the behavior can start automatically in response to your environment.

There might be times when masking keeps you safe. If you were punished or mistreated for stimming or talking about your special interests, for example, you might have masked those things in order to prevent people from harming you further. In a general sense, many nonautistic people mask from time to time. They might act differently at work than when they are with their friends. Whatever someone needs to do in order to feel and be safe is okay and valid.

At the same time, long-term masking can be exhausting, so it is helpful to learn to unmask so you can prevent burnout in the future. Knowing who you are when you are fully unmasked can allow you to explore interests, stims, and self-care strategies that improve your mental health significantly. We can work together to figure out what situations are safe for you to unmask and what that looks like for you.

How Can I Unmask?

Since many autistic people start masking at an early age and do not realize when this is even happening, they may lose sight of who they are when they are not masking. As a result, unmasking is a process that can take time and energy. Additionally, unmasking can lead the client to uncover needs that they previously ignored because it was not safe to be open about these needs. Becoming disconnected from unmet needs for the sake of self-preservation is a form of masking.

Since many autistic people are unable to fully unmask in all situations, they may struggle to unmask even when it is safe to do so. Switching between masking and unmasking can be difficult, and unmasking involves acknowledging unmet needs, making those needs more difficult to ignore. Each person will determine their own preferences and needs around unmasking, including when and how they feel safe unmasking. Your job is simply to help them understand their options and determine what conclusion is best for them.

Sample Script

Learning how to unmask is a process that can take time because you might not even know what unmasking looks like for you. It might have been so long since you were able to be fully and authentically yourself. That's okay. You can take as long as you need to figure all of this out. It is also okay if you do not feel safe unmasking in certain situations or with certain people—only *you* get to decide when and where you feel comfortable exploring this part of yourself. Here are some ways you can practice unmasking:

- **Stim on purpose:** Many autistic people force themselves to stop stimming (or are forced by someone in their environment). You might try researching stims that others in the autistic community have shared and do those stims yourself to see how they feel for you.

- **Change your food, clothes, lighting, or other environmental factors:** Sometimes autistic people are bothered by sensory things that nonautistic people don't even notice at all. You might notice that you've been tolerating things that are actually really unpleasant for you. It is okay to not wear fabrics that you don't like, to decline eating foods that you do not enjoy, and so on—even if other people like or don't mind those things. Try out different sensory experiences, and really pay attention to your unique experience.

- **Create a sensory-friendly space:** You can create a space in your home that is sensory-friendly and that has sensory items that help you self-regulate. (See the *Personalized Sensory-Friendly Space* intervention on page 58 for more details on how to make this happen.)

- **Spend time alone:** If you masked as a result of shame or mistreatment, it can help to spend time by yourself to see how you behave when you do not have to "perform" for others or meet their expectations.

- **Reevaluate the things you like:** Pay attention to the activities you enjoy doing with other people. Do you like these activities because of how they make you feel, or are you performing for other people? If you notice that you want to be "the kind of person who likes doing _____," that might be a sign that you are masking rather than truly enjoying it.

- **Pay attention to how you talk to yourself:** Not everyone experiences an internal monologue, but if you do, notice what thoughts come up for you. Notice when you might have internalized other people's negative feedback, ableism, and mistreatment. It can take a long time to rewire your thoughts to reject those negative and unfair inner voices, but you deserve to truly enjoy things without shame. Remember, if it's not hurting anyone, it's fine to enjoy it!

- **Consider "childlike" interests:** Although people talk about "outgrowing" interests as they get older, there is no age limit on things you like! Many autistic people have interests and hobbies that nonautistic people might label "childlike" or "immature." If you enjoy it, it's age appropriate.

Ongoing therapy with an affirming provider can help you work through this process and get to know yourself better.

I Have a Diagnosis—Now What?

Following an autism diagnosis, adults get almost no ongoing support or resources. Parents and guardians of autistic children get information and options that center nonaffirming and often harmful care, so even the resources that do exist are often unhelpful at best and harmful at worst. In fact, half of autistic people feel that they did not receive adequate professional support following their diagnosis, and 55 percent of parents and caregivers feel that their autistic loved one did not get adequate support (Bonnello, 2022). This demonstrates the need for providing better resources post-diagnosis.

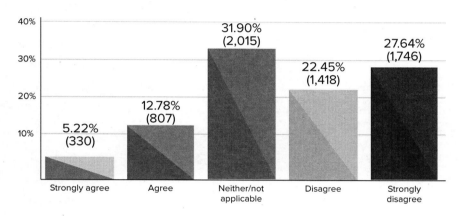

"I had the professional support that I needed post-diagnosis." [Autistic respondents]

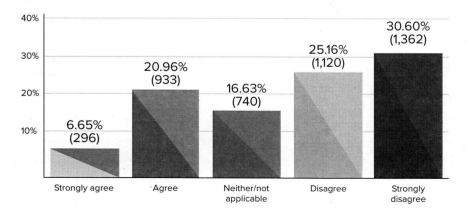

"My relative had the support they needed post-diagnosis." [Parents/caregivers]

From *Results and Analysis of the Autistic Not Weird 2022 Autism Survey* (https://autisticnotweird.com/autismsurvey).
Copyright © 2022 by Chris Bonnello. Reprinted with permission.

You are in a unique position to give autistic clients and their caregivers good, affirming information. The resource list provided at the end of this book is a great starting point, but it may not always be ideal to give your client the full list, as this can be overwhelming. You can choose resources based on their primary questions and concerns. Remember to also keep your own database up to date, as new resources will continue to emerge after this book is published, and it is not possible to get every single resource in one place. Additionally, keep a list of local resources that your client might benefit from. For example, know which occupational therapy clinics and therapists in your area specialize in supporting autistic people and are neurodiversity-affirming.

Since the specific resources you share will depend on each autistic person's needs, there is not a sample script for how to present them. Work with each client to determine what the best fit is for them moving forward.

If Trauma Symptoms Can Look Like Autism, How Do You Tell Them Apart?

Past research on autism has failed to account for the overlap of autism and trauma, so many traits that are associated with autism actually reflect the experience of stressed-out or traumatized autistic people (e.g., masking to be seen as neurotypical is similar to a traumatic fawning response). Some in the autistic community have even argued that we cannot say with certainty what autistic people look like without trauma, since so many autistic people are traumatized by existing in a world not built for their needs. While it is difficult and not always helpful to try to section someone off into different parts, like autism versus trauma, clients understandably wonder about this. The following script can help you navigate this discussion, though part of this conversation should involve time to process their emotions or questions around this topic.

Sample Script

Many autistic people have trauma history and symptoms related to that trauma. You are a whole person, and an autistic person, so it might not even be possible to "separate" these parts. However, we can explore your experience of trauma as an autistic person. If you have a specific time when your trauma began, you might note autistic traits that started before the trauma occurred and trauma responses that started afterward. That might be a place where we can tease out the differences between autistic traits and trauma responses. This might be a long journey, and I hope I can help you as you get to know yourself better.

What Is Overstimulation?

Overstimulation occurs when someone's sensory input is flooded with information, which can impact their ability to process the information accurately. Since autistic people have different sensory experiences than nonautistic people, they are at higher risk for overstimulation and can become overstimulated more often or more easily. Overstimulation can look like a sudden increase in sensitivity to certain stimuli, irritability, or a sudden need to leave an area.

Because autistic people are often taught to ignore their needs, or that their needs will not be met, they may disconnect from their sensory experiences. However, this does not make the need go away. Unaddressed overstimulation can eventually reach a breaking point during which the autistic person has a meltdown (an outburst that appears sudden and unprovoked) or goes into a state of shutdown (sudden inability to interact, speak, or communicate).

Traditional "treatment" approaches for autism focus on punishing the autistic person for having a meltdown, but since the overwhelm is out of that person's control, this is ineffective. Instead, the priority is to keep the autistic person safe in the midst of a meltdown. Over the long term, the goal is to identify meltdown triggers and help the autistic person manage these triggers in a healthy way before they reach a breaking point. Understanding overstimulation is key for clients in unmasking and in learning how to address their needs in a healthy way.

Sample Script

Everyone gets overwhelmed sometimes. Since many autistic people have sensory sensitivities, you might be more likely to get overwhelmed. Indicators that you are experiencing overwhelm include an urge to cover your eyes or ears, increased irritability, physical restlessness, anxiety or panic, physical discomfort, or sudden exhaustion. If you notice that you are starting to feel overwhelmed, you can take steps to change or reduce the sensory input around you before the feeling gets too strong. For example, you can dim the lighting, put on noise-canceling headphones, or use a sensory coping skill, like wearing a weighted blanket, playing with stim toy, or watching media that you find calming.

However, if you have been masking for a long time, you might have become disconnected from your sensory needs. If you become overstimulated and do not address that feeling—meaning you stay in the overwhelming situation—the overwhelm can get worse rather than better. You can't address a need by ignoring it. If you have ever had a time where you were suddenly extremely uncomfortable and agitated, and you couldn't bring yourself down from that feeling, that might be a sign that you were in sensory overwhelm, and it finally got to a point where you could not ignore it any longer.

When autistic people become overstimulated, they may melt down or shut down. An autistic meltdown is a behavioral outburst that parents sometimes misinterpret as a "temper tantrum." In fact, an autistic meltdown is a sign of extreme distress and overwhelm, and an autistic person may not be fully in control of their behavior during the meltdown. It can include crying, yelling, stimming, aggression, and self-harm. We want to help figure out what causes meltdowns for you so that you can prevent them. If a meltdown happens, know that this does not make you a bad person, and we can come up with a plan to help you keep yourself safe until the meltdown passes.

In addition to meltdowns, some autistic people shut down when they are overstimulated. It can feel like when you try to start a car when the gas tank is empty and the engine won't turn over. In this state, you might not be able to communicate verbally or at all, and you might struggle to understand or make sense of what others are communicating to you. As with meltdowns, we want to identify your triggers so you can avoid reaching the point of shutdown. And if a shutdown occurs, we want to have a plan in place to make sure you are safe and taken care of until it passes.

Will My Child Ever Behave Like Their Nonautistic Peers?

Many people enter parenthood with specific expectations for their child, so it is common for parents of autistic children, particularly those who are not autistic themselves, to experience grief and mourning upon learning that their child is autistic. While all feelings are valid, we want to address the parents' feelings and help them process these feelings so they can show up for their autistic child in a healthy way. This includes managing expectations and adjusting the parent's definition of "success" for their child. When a parent mourns a child who is still alive because the child does not meet their expectations, it can be incredibly traumatic for the child, who may feel rejected and unloved.

Since autistic children do not behave the same way as nonautistic children, they might not engage in neurotypical behaviors or have the same ways of showing affection, and parents may have feelings of disappointment around this. In fact, one of the supposed benefits of ABA therapy is that children who have undergone ABA begin hugging, making eye contact, and saying "I love you" to their parents when they have not previously done this. Parents who do not understand that there are different ways of showing communication and expressing affection often feel like this treatment made their child care for them—not realizing the stress and possible trauma they caused in rejecting their child's natural communication style.

Forcing autistic children to communicate in ways that are uncomfortable or unnatural for them is stressful, is traumatic, and can lead to burnout. Therefore, a neurodiversity-affirming approach would emphasize finding communication methods for the parent and child that fit the child's needs and educating the parent about responding to these methods in an appropriate and healthy way. It is the parent's job as the adult and caregiver to meet their child's needs rather than expecting the child to change to meet the parent's needs.

This is often a point of contention in autism communities, with parents feeling invalidated when they are told to let go of the expectation that their child show affection in a specific way. Once again, neurodiversity-affirming professionals can relate to parents where they are and validate their emotions while simultaneously providing appropriate education around how to best care for their autistic loved one.

Sample Script

It sounds like you are worried that your autistic child will not behave or communicate in the way you expected when you became a parent. While your feelings are valid, remember that your child needs you. We can find appropriate support to help you work through your emotions and honor your feelings in a way that is healthy for you and protects your child. You are grieving who your child never was, and if your child feels rejected by you because of this, that could be very hurtful to them. Think about it—would you rather your child feel safe with you, or present themselves in a way that hurts them in order to meet your expectations?

Your parents might have made you feel like you weren't good enough for them as a child, but you have an opportunity to break that cycle by learning to love and accept your child for who they are. That is a wonderful and beautiful thing. It is okay to have your own emotions and to get support for those emotions, while honoring, affirming, and accepting your child for exactly who they are.

Everyone expresses and receives love in their own way. Autistic people often communicate in ways that neurotypical people see as unusual or different. It might take some learning and adjusting to be able to communicate with your child in the ways that work for them. Know that even if your child never shows affection in the specific way you imagined, they still care about you, and you can still connect with them in the way that is safe and comfortable for them.

Sensory Interventions: Movement-Based

Since autistic people have different sensory needs, therapy interventions that tap into and meet these sensory needs are important in providing affirming care. Many stims are movement-based, and many autistic people are kinetic sensory-seeking, meaning they are most comfortable when moving in some way versus sitting perfectly still. Autistic people are also more likely than nonautistic people to have ADHD, often experiencing hyperactive symptoms that necessitate movement-based activities. Additionally, since trauma can cause someone to lose touch with their body, movement-based activities can be highly beneficial to those with trauma symptoms, as they help with getting back in touch with the body and its needs.

For some, being forced to remain still can interfere with processing. An autistic person who needs to move but is required to stay still might use all their energy to remain still, leaving them unable to process anything else. This can limit their ability to focus in many environments; for example, it can prevent them from listening in the classroom or from fully being present in their therapy session.

Given the importance of movement for many autistic individuals, the interventions in this section focus on incorporating movement into your sessions. While some might argue that these interventions are most appropriate for children because they contain aspects of play, remember that many autistic adults have interests that are sometimes labeled as childlike, and any activity that they find beneficial is age appropriate as long as it does not harm them. In fact, encouraging an autistic adult to pursue "childish" interests might help them overcome feelings of shame and unmask.

PERSONALIZED SENSORY-FRIENDLY SPACE

ALL AGES

Earlier in this section, I discussed ways to create a sensory-friendly space in your office that clients can use to experiment with sensory items and get to know their own sensory needs better. To take this a step further, you can help clients develop an individualized sensory space in their own home designed with their needs in mind. The goal is to create a place where they feel safe and their sensory needs are met. They can use this space to unwind and feel comfortable and to self-regulate when they feel overwhelmed or escalated.

When helping a client create a sensory space, you will likely discuss their needs in session and have them put the space together in between appointments, reporting back about what did and did not work so you can problem-solve any hiccups together. If you are engaging in telehealth or in-home services, you can help with the setup during the appointment and even see the client from their sensory space if they are comfortable with this. As you work with your client, encourage them to develop the space over time as they learn more about their needs.

Note: If the autistic person is a minor or has a legal guardian, involve the guardian in the process of making a sensory space. The parent or guardian needs to understand that this is a space specifically for the autistic person and that they cannot make changes to the space without the autistic person specifically requesting it. They must also understand that, since the space is designed to meet sensory needs, *it is not a privilege to use the sensory space. Rather, it is a need.* Access to the sensory space must not be restricted as "punishment" for misbehavior, and the autistic person should never have to "earn" access to the space. Sensory spaces create emotional and psychological safety, which are needs just like food, clothing, and shelter. Taking away a sensory space as a consequence is the same as denying someone food as a consequence. It is a form of abuse.

Additionally, many "problem behaviors" that autistic people exhibit are rooted in sensory needs going unmet. An autistic person who does not have adequate space to get their sensory needs met is at risk for meltdowns and shutdowns, which can consist of verbal and physical aggression and even self-harm behavior. Access to a safe sensory space can actually reduce these behaviors while simultaneously improving the autistic person's sense of safety and their mental health.

Here are the steps for creating a personalized sensory space:

1. **Identify a location.** Have the client (and their guardian, if applicable) determine a location in the home they can use as a sensory space. Depending on the size of the home and the number of people living in the space, it can be challenging to carve out a spot just for one person. Of

course, if this intervention is not a fit for a given client, that is okay—no one suggestion will be universally applicable. However, you can also get creative in finding space if the client feels they would benefit from this. For example, a client who feels secure in small spaces might love having a sensory space under their bed! In determining a location for a sensory space, consider:

    a. **Is the space private?** The autistic person should be able to feel comfortable unmasking in the space and have adequate privacy to do so.

    b. **Is the size of the space sufficient?** The autistic person must have adequate room to stim if needed and to keep any sensory items needed in the space.

    c. **Can the space go unused by others?** Consistency is important to many autistic people, and their sensory space needs to be theirs alone.

2. **Stock the space.** If you have stocked your office with various sensory items, clients can experiment with these options to figure out their sensory preferences. Remember that many people with sensory sensitivities have some combination of sensory-seeking and sensory-avoidant behaviors. Someone might have a strong negative reaction to one sensation but be sensory-seeking with something else. This can make it difficult to identify what sensory items would be a good fit. Use the *Interoception and Mindful Awareness* exercises later in this chapter to help your client identify what sensory items they want in their space.

3. **Make adjustments.** Sensory needs can and do change over time. Prepare your client (and their guardian, if applicable) so they are not surprised if this occurs. Have them reassess the space and make changes as needed.

4. **Practice using the space.** Due to masking behaviors, some autistic people lose touch with their needs. The goal of the sensory space is to give the autistic person space to self-regulate and get their sensory needs met, but if they are unaware of those needs, they might not know how to use the space effectively. Here are some strategies they can try:

    a. **Schedule sensory breaks.** Have the client set aside time to spend in their sensory space. Normalize using the space so it does not feel like a punishment or redirection to enter the space.

    b. **Make a plan for offering support.** If the client has a legal guardian or lives with a loved one, and they are comfortable involving this person in their treatment, develop a plan for the loved one to support the client in using their sensory space. As the client works on identifying their sensory needs, their loved one might be able to help cue them to these needs. For example, if the client begins stimming a certain way when they are becoming overwhelmed, the loved one can help bring their attention to this. Make sure that this is presented in a neutral and helpful way—being cued to use the sensory space is *not* a punishment or indication that the client is doing something wrong!

    c. **Use the space before it's needed.** While a sensory space can help an autistic person regulate when they are struggling, it can also just help their overall mental health. If properly tailored to their needs, it should be a space that they enjoy and want to spend time in.

    d. **Notice what feelings the space brings up.** Simply spending time in the sensory space and noticing what comes up can help the client identify their sensory needs and tailor the space to meet them. If it helps, the client can reflect on how they feel in the space. This can help them further develop the space to meet their needs.

5. **Use the *Sensory Space Reflection Log*.** The enclosed log can help your client become more aware of how they respond to the sensory space and allow them to tweak the space to meet their needs. When the client uses the space, have them note the date and time, as well as what triggering event brought on the need to use the space. Of course, the "triggering event" column can be left blank if they were simply using the space preemptively or because they felt like it. Ask them to note the details of what was positive or negative about the experience so they can modify the space based on their needs.

SENSORY SPACE REFLECTION LOG

Day and Time	Triggering Event (if applicable)	Positive Sensory Experiences	Negative Sensory Experiences

THERAPEUTIC TWISTER

AGES 6+

While movement-based activities can help an individual get back in touch with their body following trauma, a sudden awareness of one's body sensations can be overwhelming. This is particularly true of autistic people who might feel their emotions more intensely than nonautistics due to sensory issues or for whom communicating emotional needs is a challenge.

This is where the classic game of Twister can come in handy, as it challenges players to balance and take on atypical and often uncomfortable positions without falling over. This in itself can have therapeutic benefit, even by simply incorporating cues to "notice your muscles stretching" or "hold your focus to keep from falling." For clients who either prefer or require more nondirective interventions, this can help them become more aware of their body's position in space, notice what their muscles are doing, and gain control over their movements.

In an individual session, take turns playing the game with your client, with one of you on the mat and the other spinning and calling out commands. Going back and forth in this manner has the added benefit of helping clients practice communicating and receiving instructions. In family sessions, the client and their family members may take to the mat at the same time if this is appropriate and if the client is comfortable doing so. Otherwise, you can rotate who is on the mat.

For clients who are learning more about emotions, a variation of the game is to discuss times you have felt different emotions when different colors come up. Suggested feelings to discuss can include:

- Red for anger
- Blue for sadness
- Green for fear
- Yellow for happiness

Another therapeutic variation is to use prompts from The Ungame or another therapeutic or feelings board game. The person spinning answers a question for each move that the person on the mat makes, fostering more conversation and exploration of emotions while engaging in the body work game.

Remember that the activity itself can be therapeutic without these additions, although added layers can tap into other therapeutic skills. If you propose an added twist but the client expresses that they prefer to play classic Twister, the most affirming thing you can do is honor their request, as this teaches them assertiveness and autonomy.

FULL BODY STRETCHES

It can feel so good to stretch out our muscles. For some, the sensory experience of stretching various muscles also instills a sense of relaxation and relief. This is not to mention that regular stretching can improve blood flow, joint range of motion, muscle efficiency, and overall mobility as well as reduce risk for physical injury. Some of the medical issues that autistic people experience, including connective tissue disorder, pain issues, and problems with mobility, can benefit from regular stretching too. Additionally, an emotionally neutral activity such as stretching can foster mindful awareness of body sensations. By focusing on the stretches themselves, the client becomes aware of these sensations without the therapist directly pointing them out.

The stretches included in this section are examples of activities that you might incorporate in session but are not a comprehensive list. Choose stretches that work for each client, based on their preferences and any mobility limitations. When possible, give the client options, and let them choose which combination of stretches they want to do. You can follow their lead or choose positions together. If the client asks for help choosing, you can certainly offer support in this way, but giving the client the option to choose can improve their engagement in the activity.

Safety note: It can be helpful to warm up with walking or another movement-based activity for 5 to 10 minutes before stretching. You and your client can aim to hold each pose for about 20 to 30 seconds, but listen to your body cues and release sooner if there is any pain. Always follow physician guidance in determining what activities are healthy and appropriate. In addition, those who experience hypermobility might have the ability to extend stretches farther than is physically safe. Again, always follow physician guidance in choosing safe and appropriate activities, and ensure that you and your client are not overextending yourselves in a way that could cause injury.

Sphinx Stretch

Lie on the floor on your stomach. Place your elbows beneath your shoulders with your arms extended forward and your palms touching the ground. Rest your feet slightly apart behind you, with your toes pointed in a comfortable position. Lift your head and chest, gently stretching your lower back, butt, and thighs. Press your hips into the floor, and breathe deeply while you feel the stretch from your neck, down your back, all the way to your toes.

Side Stretch

Either stand or sit with a straight back and long neck. If standing, place your feet slightly farther than shoulder-width apart. Raise one arm straight up over your head and lean to the opposite side, feeling the stretch all the way down your arm and ribs. You can raise both arms and pull the arm you are stretching using your other hand to deepen the stretch. Repeat on the other side.

Torso Stretch

Either standing with feet shoulder-width apart or sitting with a straight back and neck, raise both hands directly over your head. Keeping your shoulders down, link your fingers, and press your palms toward the ceiling while breathing deeply.

V-Stretch

Sitting on the floor, put your legs straight in front of you, with your feet flexed so that your toes point toward the ceiling. Straighten your back, then lean gently forward, reaching your arms toward your toes. Know that it is okay if you can reach your toes, your calves, your knees, or even your thighs. Just lean until you feel the stretch, wherever that is.

Lunge Stretch

Stand with one foot in front of the other. Bend the knee on your front leg and shift your weight forward, keeping your back foot on the ground. You can put your hands at your side or on your knee for balance. You can lean slightly forward or go into a deep lunge, where your back knee almost touches the ground. You can complete lunge stretches on each side as well as in front of you.

BALANCE BALL ACTIVITY

AGES 5+

Balance balls are large, round, elastic balls that vary in size and firmness. You can adjust the firmness by adding air or letting air out, and your client can experiment with the ball to figure out what sensory experience fits them best.

If a client is kinetic sensory-seeking, consider offering a balance ball rather than a traditional chair during sessions. This will let them engage their entire body while remaining seated for the session. This can be helpful when the client wants or needs to verbally process something but struggles to engage when sitting still and gets distracted when engaging in a secondary activity.

Clients can also roll or bounce on the ball to engage their core muscles and bring awareness to these muscle groups. If you are working on internal or external body awareness, this activity can draw attention to the sensations inside the body and, with proper direction, awareness of where the body is in space. Additionally, clients who are practicing different stim behaviors to see what helps them regulate can try different bouncing and rocking activities using the ball.

Simply having the balance ball available for clients to experiment with sends the message that you are flexible in what "sitting down" for therapy looks like, affirming the client's different sensory and movement needs.

SPINNING CHAIR

AGES 5+

If your office contains a chair that can spin, this is an easy activity you can do with your clients. Simply invite the client to sit in the chair with any sensory items they want with them (such as a soft blanket or stuffed animal). They can then choose whether to spin themselves or have you spin them while they sit. Encourage them to share any body sensations that come up while they spin or any images that come into their mind.

Note that any activities that involve spinning can be overwhelming for some, especially those prone to motion sickness, so talk to your client to determine the appropriateness of this intervention. You don't want anyone vomiting in the middle of their session! If a client likes spinning activities but sometimes gets overstimulated or nauseous, they can still do this activity with a timer to make sure they stop before they become overwhelmed. Always check in and encourage the client to let you know at any point when an activity has stopped working for them.

WALKING THERAPY

AGES 10+

Not only is getting outside a great way to engage the full body, but for many, simply being outside can improve their mood. If your office is in a walkable area that is accessible to your clients, or if your office building has a walkable space, taking a walk during your sessions can be a neurodiversity-affirming intervention. Walking is particularly helpful for autistic people who are uncomfortable with eye contact or who become overwhelmed if they feel the need to attend to their facial expressions while talking. Walking together takes the pressure off nonverbal cues, since you and your client are not directly facing each other. Additionally, as with the balance ball, walking during the session allows for movement without distracting from the topic at hand.

Of course, not everyone has the option to go outside during their session. Depending on the location of your office and your policies, going outside might not be permissible or safe. Additionally, clients with mobility issues or who use particular mobility aids might not be able to easily or comfortably walk alongside you. Make sure you get appropriate consent for any therapy that takes place outside of your closed office, both for any liabilities in case of injury and with awareness of any possible confidentiality limitations resulting from the intervention.

SENSORY SWINGS

AGES 3+

A sensory swing is a particular type of swing that moves and rotates in specific ways with the intent of helping with self-regulation and sensory-seeking. Occupational and physical therapists sometimes use sensory swings to help their patients develop motor skills and muscles. Like other movement-based activities, sensory swings also increase awareness of body movement and position in space.

Having a sensory swing in your office can allow clients to engage in sensory work and get their sensory needs met during their appointments with you. You can use the swing like a balance ball by inviting clients to simply sit in the swing and move while they talk through various topics. You can also encourage the client to engage in swinging while attending to their muscles, their internal body cues, or the location of their body in space. If possible, clients who benefit from sensory swings might enjoy having a swing in their sensory space at home as well. However, these swings are expensive, can be difficult to install, and take up a lot of space, so this may not be an option for all clients (or for all therapists to have in their office).

When purchasing a sensory swing, make sure you choose one with weight limits that work for the clients you see. For instance, if you work with adults, make sure the swing you purchase is not for children, who weigh significantly less. There are many different kinds of sensory swings to choose from, based on what works in your space:

- **Disc swing:** A disc swing is made from a round, plastic disc suspended in the air by a rope that is secured to the center of the disc. Occupational therapists sometimes use this kind of swing to work on improving grip and core strength, but it also moves in many different ways and is relatively easy to control. Disc swings are often found on playgrounds.

- **Log swing:** As the name suggests, a log swing is made of a cylindrical piece suspended in the air. You can sit on it like a rocking horse, and it can help with developing core strength and muscle mass.

- **Mesh swing:** A mesh swing is styled like a net suspended from the ceiling, and you can decide how spread out or compact the mesh is when you set it up. It is like a small hammock, and you can sit up or lie down in it. This swing can be useful if you are engaging in another activity, like reading a book or using other fidget items while you are in the swing.

- **Saucer swing:** Sometimes called a "flying saucer swing," this swing is a large, flat circle that you can lie on and swing side to side or spin in a circle.

- **Skateboard swing:** Exactly as it sounds like, a skateboard swing is one in which the seat part of the swing is made from the deck of a skateboard. It swings side to side while you stand on it. Typically, this swing needs to be in an outdoor space for safety reasons. This swing engages different muscle groups throughout the body.

- **Stretch swing:** This swing is like a sleeping bag suspended in the air. You enter the bag, and the fabric squeezes around you. You can even pull your head inside and be fully immersed in the swing. While you are squeezed inside of the swing, you can also wiggle or move around in any way that is comfortable for you while using the swing.

BASKETBALL

AGES 3+

If your office has an outdoor space available, a regulation basketball hoop can be a fun way to engage clients in their sessions. However, if any part of your session occurs in a location where someone passing by might see or hear your conversation, ensure that you get appropriate consent, and always protect client privacy and confidentiality appropriately. Even if you do not have a full-size basketball hoop available, you can purchase a small hoop for your office. Small, stand-alone hoops or those that you can hook over the back of your door are relatively inexpensive and easy to install.

Breaking patterns and conceptions about what a therapy session "should" look like or how it "has" to be structured is an important component of crafting neurodiversity-affirming interventions that meet individual client needs rather than fitting into a preconceived therapy box. Whether you have a miniature hoop in your office or a full-size hoop outside, making your sessions fun increases client comfort and helps you build rapport. This is especially true for children and teens—who often enjoy having an athletic component to their sessions—but is also true for adults who may feel guarded or uncertain about engaging with their provider.

In addition to building a relationship between you and your client, basketball is a great way to work on focus and executive-functioning skills in session. You can even choose to incorporate a competitive piece to the game, whether by simply keeping score or engaging in a game like HORSE, which has the added benefit of introducing the client to disappointment, perceived failure, and frustration. The client can notice their emotions and behaviors in the context of a safe, therapeutic environment and work through their frustrations with you. At the same time, you can model appropriate regulation to the client when the roles are reversed.

Sensory Interventions: Music and Sound

Although there can be overlap between music-based interventions and movement-based interventions—dance can be incredibly therapeutic!—the focus of these next interventions is on the use of sound and music rather than movement. Since many autistic people struggle with communication, music interventions can help them express their emotions and needs without the use of words. Remember, too, that autistic people can experience and perceive sounds differently than nonautistic people (and, of course, everyone has a unique sensory experience!). Just like sounds can be overstimulating and lead to meltdowns, used therapeutically, music and sound can be a powerful source of self-regulation and positive sensory experiences.

In this section, you will learn how to incorporate music into your sessions in ways that are neurodiversity-affirming. What I have provided here is only a sampling of different music and other sound-based interventions, but as always, you can apply the underlying philosophy of neurodiversity-affirming therapy to other interventions you choose for your practice. For example, in addition to these interventions, you might choose to have music playing in your office if your client's sensory needs or preferences indicate that they would benefit from this.

WHAT SONG DESCRIBES YOU TODAY?

AGES 5+

Sometimes it is difficult to put into words how we are feeling, especially if we are having a hard day. Music can capture emotions in unique ways, and for autistic people who struggle to accurately identify their emotions, music may be a way for them to tap into and express these feelings. If a client has a difficult time sharing their emotions, you might consider replacing "How do you feel today?" with "What song describes you today?"

This can be a fun activity to start sessions with week after week and to track how a client's song choice shifts over time. The client might notice that they are drawn to certain songs, artists, or genres when they are struggling versus when they are having particularly positive weeks. The long-term data that you collect from this exercise provides invaluable information about how your client relates to music and the patterns that come up in their life.

When the client choses their song, listen to it together, and prompt the client to sit with how they feel and to notice what they experience in their body while they listen. You can model this body awareness by sharing how you feel and describing your emotional response to the song. If the song has a solid beat, you can incorporate some dance and movement as you listen and see how this impacts how you feel.

Over time, as you and your client observe patterns, you can see if music can result in any noticeable shifts in mood. For example, on a day when a client is feeling a more melancholy song, you can experiment with playing a song that the client tends to choose when they have a lot of positive emotions. Explore how this impacts their emotions in real time as they listen to different songs.

PLAYLIST OF YOUR LIFE

AGES 8+

Because music allows us to communicate in ways that transcend words, you can learn a lot about a person (and they can learn a lot about themselves) by creating a playlist that represents their life. If you use this activity early in therapy, it can be a fun way for the client to disclose their values, memories, and emotions outside of an interview format. Over time, it can also reflect the client's personal growth.

The following pages contain questions you can ask your client to help them create their own life playlist. Separate questions are included for children and younger teens versus older teens and adults. However, you are welcome to change the list based on what works for the individual. It also includes open-ended options so the client can choose new prompts that are significant to them or simply add songs they enjoy that do not necessarily fit into a specific category. Any client old enough to understand the concept of this activity can participate in it, but you might choose to tweak the suggested list based on their developmental level.

Just like you can add prompts to the list, remember that you can skip or eliminate categories that do not apply, that the client is uncomfortable with, or that may bring up triggers the client is not yet prepared to process. For instance, if you are using this activity early in therapy to get to know a client who has significant trauma history, some of the memory prompts might be triggering, and the client might not yet have sufficient rapport with you to delve into this right away. You might choose to create a different list of questions before the client's session, and in either case, communicate to them that they can skip anything they are uncomfortable with.

Sometimes autistic people struggle with choosing a "favorite" or "best" for a category, and this can include songs. If a client is struggling with choosing between two songs, consider listing both. As the client puts together their playlist, you might choose to listen to each song together and sit with what it brings up. This might mean that the playlist takes several sessions to put together. You might also choose all of the songs at once and then go through and listen to the playlist to see how it flows.

Playlist for Your Life: Child

1. Did your parents ever sing to you when you were very little? If so, what song do you associate with this?

2. What is a place that feels very safe for you? Is there a song you associate with this place?

3. What song makes you think of home?

4. Who is a person who is very important to you? What song reminds you of them? (Repeat as necessary for multiple important people.)

5. What is a song associated with a TV show or movie that you like?

6. What is a song that always makes you want to dance?

7. What is a song that lifts your mood?

8. What is a song that reminds you of a time you felt very happy?

9. What is a song that reminds you of a time you felt sad?

10. What is a song that reminds you of a time you felt angry?

11. What is a song that reminds you of a time when you were struggling?

12. What is a song that reminds you of a challenge you overcame?

13. What is a song that reminds you of a holiday that you enjoy?

14. If you have a favorite song, what is it?

15. What other songs would help someone get to know you?

16. What other categories would you add?

Playlist for Your Life: Adolescent and Adult

1. What is a song that reminds you of your childhood?

2. What is a song that reminds you of the home you grew up in?

3. What is a song that reminds you of your hometown?

4. What is a song that reminds you of your favorite place from childhood?

5. What is a song that reminds you of when you first went to school?

6. Who is a person who was important to you while growing up, and what song reminds you of them? (Repeat as needed if the client has multiple answers.)

7. Who is a person who is important to you now, and what song reminds you of them? (Repeat as needed if the client has multiple answers.)

8. What is a song that reminds you of happiness?

9. What is a song that reminds you of sadness?

10. What is a song that reminds you of anger?

11. What is a song that reminds you of a time when you were struggling?

12. What is a song that reminds you of a challenge you overcame?

13. What song do you associate with your favorite holiday?

14. If you have a favorite song, what is it?

15. What other songs would help someone get to know you?

16. What other categories would you add?

TIMELINE PLAYLIST

AGES 10+

The songs that resonate for us can change over time. We might connect with some songs at a certain point in our lives but find that they do not stir up the same feelings as we continue to grow. For this activity, you will guide the client in exploring what songs resonated with them at different points in their history to help you and them understand their journey.

To begin this intervention, ask your client to complete the *Timeline Activity* on page 163 to map out a timeline of their past and present (if that is an activity with which they are comfortable). If not, they can choose songs to represent each year of their life, or they can break their history down into a timeline based on significant events. Don't limit yourself—clients often come up with new and creative ways to outline their life, and the direction they take with this task can be very informative!

Once the client has put together their timeline, have them choose a significant song (or many significant songs) for each section or event they listed. They can choose songs that resonated with them at the time, songs that currently remind them of that time in their life, or any other method that makes sense to them. If they want to take this a step further, they can pull specific lyrics from each song and dig into how these lyrics represent what they wish to communicate about this period.

WHAT'S YOUR THEME SONG?

AGES 5+

In movies, television shows, radio programs, and other forms of media, the theme song is the song that plays at the beginning of the program. This music immediately lets everyone know what they are listening to and tends to represent the best and most exciting features of the program. In this intervention, clients will choose an existing song that they feel represents their theme, although clients who are highly musically inclined might choose to write their own theme song instead.

Helping your client identify a personalized theme song serves two purposes: (1) It is a quick and easy way to get to know their "vibe," and (2) it is a representation of the very best in them. It gives the client a chance to develop insight as they explore their identity and focus on their individual strengths, which in turn fosters self-esteem. As the client chooses their theme song, explore with them what this song communicates about who they are. Then, expand on the discussion by highlighting their strengths and asking how the song reflects the best parts of them.

If a client really enjoys a particular television show or piece of media that has a theme song, they might choose that song to represent them. What is it about the show that this client enjoys? Is there a particular character that they relate to, and what does that character have in common with the client? How would the client like to be more like that character? People often see themselves in fictional characters, and asking these follow-up questions can help the client tie this into an understanding of themselves.

BEST SONG FOR . . .

Music can have a powerful impact on your mood—amping you up when you want to feel excited, comforting you when you feel down, and so much more. People also turn to music to reflect and validate how they already feel in a given situation. For some, listening to a song on repeat is a stim that can prevent meltdowns and burnout. In this activity, the client will create a list of songs that they can use to cope with various situations and emotions. These can be songs that help them deal with triggers or that allow them to manage overstimulation. When a client is escalated, it can be difficult for them to remember the skills, techniques, and tools that bring them out of that headspace. By making this list in advance, the client is better able to use music to process and move through difficult emotions.

If the client has a parent, guardian, or other loved one who helps them when they are struggling, work with that person to prompt the client to use their songs when they are having trouble. Help the client and their loved one work together to identify ways that the loved one can point out that the autistic person might benefit from this coping skill in a way that is nonjudgmental, does not indicate that the client is in trouble or doing something wrong, and gently guides them to use an appropriate skill. It can help to simply have a code word to cue this, like *music*, so the autistic person checks in with themselves and thinks to use the skill. However, it is often better if the loved one presents the prompt as a question or suggestion rather than a command so as not to trigger any defensiveness.

The list that follows can help you brainstorm songs to include in the client's coping repertoire, but as always, this list is not an end-all; it is merely a starting point. Let clients include additional categories they think will help them, and make sure they understand that they can skip any prompts that do not apply.

Best Songs For . . .

1. When I feel angry: _____

2. When I feel sad: _____

3. When I feel overstimulated: _____

4. When it has been a long day: _____

5. When I feel tired: _____

6. When I want to feel calmer: _____

7. When I want to feel happier: _____

8. When I want to sit with a big feeling: _____

9. When I feel misunderstood: _____

10. When I need a short break: _____

11. Other situations: _____

SONGS THAT MAKE ME FEEL …

AGES 5+

While the previous activity is intended to help clients use music to manage emotions and overstimulation, this activity is simply about fostering self-awareness. Clients who feel "ordered around" by coping skills activities may find this intervention more comfortable. For this activity, the client simply chooses a song associated with each emotion. The list in this activity is a starting point for clients to identify songs that elicit certain emotions. As always, encourage them to skip any emotions they do not want to answer or to add feelings not on the initial list.

While it may be tempting to encourage clients to push themselves to focus on emotions they want to skip, an affirming standpoint recognizes that the client is the expert on themselves and their needs. Since many autistic people are used to people ignoring their needs or telling them that their needs are wrong, it is essential to empower the client to communicate what they need in the moment by both listening to them and honoring that communication. It is healing and therapeutic when a client knows their therapist prioritizes their comfort over what the therapist feels an intervention "should" look like. In other words—respect your client's "no."

At the same time, you can certainly ask about the client's discomfort. It can be beneficial to understand what it is about the intervention or emotion that the client does not want to dig into, as this can inform your suggestions for other interventions. It can also let you know if the client is saying, "This is not a fit for me" or "This is not something I have the capacity for today but am open to digging into in the future." These are just some of the ways that this intervention can help you build rapport with your client, develop insight into their needs, and foster an affirming treatment environment.

Songs That Make Me Feel . . .

1. Happy: _____

2. Sad: _____

3. Angry: _____

4. Scared: _____

5. Excited: _____

6. Calm: _____

7. Agitated: _____

8. Embarrassed: _____

9. Affectionate: _____

10. Loving: _____

11. Confident: _____

12. Fearful: _____

13. Anxious: _____

14. Lonely: _____

15. Enraged: _____

16. Cringey: _____

17. Annoyed: _____

18. Woeful: _____

19. Bored: _____

20. Nostalgic: _____

CHANGING THE LYRICS

AGES 5+

Since a client may no longer resonate with a song that they used to connect with at a certain point in their life, rewriting that song so its lyrics reflect where the client is now can highlight that growth, especially when their day-to-day experiences do not reflect long-term changes. For some autistic people, sameness is important. They might listen to the same song, watch the same show or movie, and consume the same art over long periods of time. This is okay, and there is absolutely nothing wrong with liking something for a long time! If they are wondering about their personal growth over time, this activity allows them to explore this growth while still using the same melody that they enjoy.

To begin, print or write out the lyrics to the client's chosen song. You can process the lyrics and talk about how they used to resonate with the client if this is helpful, then explore how the client would change the words to better reflect who they are now. If you are musically inclined, or your client is, you can play or sing the updated song together when you finish. For a less intense intervention, clients can also simply reword the song in ways that they find amusing or fun. This can foster creativity and build rapport with you.

DRUMMING TO REDIRECT HURTFUL STIMS

ALL AGES

Using drums to create music can be an effective way to redirect harmful stims like hitting or head banging. Stims that involve tapping, thumping, or banging already create a drumming sound, so the use of actual drums for stim behaviors is a natural redirection that clients can use as an alternative. However, when someone is escalated, they may have a difficult time receiving redirection, so it is important that you take steps to keep them safe in the moment and only bring up alternatives when they are calm. Above all, you want to present the activity in a nonjudgmental and caring way. You might use a variation on the following:

> I know sometimes it's hard for you to control your body, especially when you are overwhelmed and overstimulated. I am going to do my best to help you and try to prevent you from getting that upset, but I know sometimes things happen that are out of our control. *You are not in trouble, and no one is angry with you.* But when you [*hurtful stim*], you might get injured. Because the most important thing is for you to be safe, it could help us to practice another behavior that lets you get that overwhelming feeling out in a way that won't hurt your body.

Then encourage the client to practice drumming, possibly on a schedule, to let them get in the habit and learn what styles and movements help them self-regulate. Make sure that the drum is accessible to them at all times. You also want to help the client learn to identify when they are starting to escalate and encourage them to use this skill in that moment. Again, any prompts to use the drum in the moment should be presented calmly and nonjudgmentally:

> This situation is getting difficult for you. I am so sorry. [*Possibly note what cues the client is giving off to indicate that they are struggling.*] Maybe we can do some stims to help you feel better in this moment.

SINGING

Just like listening to a song can change how we feel, singing a song can have a similar impact. When we sing, we take deep breaths, which can reduce agitation and arousal. It is for this reason that therapists and other mental health professionals often encourage clients to practice deep breathing. However, some clients struggle with anything perceived as a command, and specifically being prompted to breathe or "take a breath" can be triggering. Many autistic people who have been ridiculed or punished for becoming overstimulated might be used to hearing "take a breath" when they start to become overwhelmed. If the intent of that prompt is punishment, correction, or shame, they may understandably associate prompts to breathe with being "in trouble" or doing something "bad" and "wrong."

Instead, work with your client to choose songs that are soothing to them (possibly by using the other activities in this section) and sing them together to get the benefits of deep breathing. When people sing, they exhale more slowly than when they are just breathing (even mindful breathing). You might choose to have your client practice this activity in between sessions to get in the habit, and have their caregivers or trusted loved ones say, "Let's sing together!" when they experience a trigger. This can prompt de-escalation in a fun, nonshaming way.

RAIN STICKS

ALL AGES

A rain stick is a musical instrument constructed with a hollow tube that is filled with small objects (like rice, pins, or pebbles). Some cultures use rain sticks made from cacti or other plants for ritualistic purposes. There are also children's toy rain sticks made from plastic or other materials. These instruments make a sound like rain falling when they're shaken or turned over, making them a great stim item for autistic people who find sounds soothing. You can use the rain sticks to make music together as a joint in-session activity or simply let the client manipulate the rain stick to help them self-regulate at their own pace.

SINGING BOWLS

AGES 8+

A singing bowl is a bowl-shaped bell played by tapping or running a mallet around its outer or inner rim. Bowls of different sizes make tones at different pitches. Playing or listening to a singing bowl can instill feelings of relaxation and calm, so it's a great activity to start a session (centering you and your client and bringing your attention to the current moment) or to end a session (providing a gentle transition when it is time to stop for today). You can play the bowl, using tones and dings to prompt different meditation exercises, or let the client guide the activity by playing the bowl.

Note: While the vibrations and sounds generated by singing bowls can be soothing and relaxing for many, they can trigger seizures in individuals with epilepsy. Autistic people are at higher risk for epilepsy than the general population, so make sure you have taken a thorough medical history, and never use singing bowls if contraindicated.

Sensory Interventions: Tactile

Autistic people have different experiences when it comes to touch and tactile sensations. Sometimes they feel discomfort, irritation, or even pain in response to textures that do not cause visible injury. As a result, many autistic people experience gaslighting and invalidation of their experience. For instance, an autistic person who finds jeans uncomfortable might be told, "You're fine. Those pants are not uncomfortable." On the other hand, some autistic people are sensory-seeking and experience strong, positive feelings from different tactile experiences. For instance, they may feel most comfortable in tight clothing that feels like it is squeezing them. However, an individual's sensory environment might not be conducive to these sensory-seeking behaviors, and they might experience ridicule or backlash as a result.

In addition, autistic people often do not habituate to tactile sensations, meaning they do not adjust to a new sensation over time. Most nonautistic people are not aware of how their clothing feels on their body throughout the day, but for many autistic people, they remain aware of these sensations all the time. When an autistic person is repeatedly told that their experience is wrong or that their perception of reality is incorrect, they learn to question their experience by default and may even lose touch with their body. This is a form of dissociation that, while unhealthy in the long term, develops out of necessity. If someone cannot get their needs met, they will just feel frustrated and angry when they are aware of these needs, so it feels better to pretend the needs do not exist. At the same time, ignoring a need does not make the need go away. Eventually, the need becomes so intense and urgent that it can no longer be ignored. This can lead to meltdowns, shutdowns, and even burnout.

Tactile therapy interventions create space for clients to explore different sensations and get back in touch with their tactile sensory needs. Clients can learn to consciously recognize their tactile experiences and make adjustments so they are more comfortable. Additionally, certain interventions can help rewire the brain to recognize when a sensory experience is not fundamentally harmful. While neurodiversity-affirming providers prioritize the client's comfort and do not want to force clients to tolerate discomfort in the name of convenience to those around them, there are times that tactile sensory sensitivities can cause problems and harm.

For example, some autistic people are very sensitive to the feel of fabric on their arms or legs and prefer to wear tank tops and shorts. This is, of course, their decision. However, if they live in a very cold climate, there may be times when it is unsafe for them to leave their home without arm and leg coverings. This might necessitate learning to tolerate these coverings for health reasons. Clients can work to train their brain to tolerate and even find these coverings comfortable, but they should still be allowed to choose what fabrics and coverings are best for them.

The following activities can help you address tactile sensory needs with autistic clients from a neurodiversity-affirming standpoint.

WEIGHTED VEST OR BLANKET

VEST: AGES 5+

BLANKET: AGES 3+

A weighted vest is a vest that is made from heavy fabric or that has several sewn-in pockets containing weighted items like sand, bars, or beads. These vests can weigh as little as four pounds or as much as 40 or more pounds. Similarly, a weighted blanket has weighted pockets sewn in to add weight. Weighted blankets can be small enough to fit in your lap, large enough to cover a king-sized bed, or any size in between. They can weigh just a few pounds or more than 40 pounds. Generally, it is recommended to use weights that are 10 percent of the user's body weight or less.

Those who are sensory-seeking for pressure on their muscles, joints, or whole body often find these items relaxing and calming. Some autistic people use a weighted blanket to improve their sleep or a weighted vest to de-escalate and prevent a meltdown when they are struggling. While there are resources to create your own weighted blanket or vest online, they are also available for purchase. It can be helpful to keep a small weighted blanket in your office so that clients can get a feel for their sensory experience with weighted clothing or coverings. However, individuals with mobility issues who cannot independently take a weighted vest or blanket off should not use these items without supervision for safety reasons.

WEIGHTS

In addition to blankets and vests, there are many other weighted items that can tap into autistic sensory needs and help with issues like difficulty with fine motor control. You can toss soft, weighted therapy balls back and forth to engage the client's muscles and improve coordination, or place weighted grips on pencils and pens to help with handwriting. Hand weights can also ground the client in the present moment and the therapy space, helping them engage in the process fully.

For some, the added weight can be distressing, so it is helpful to try out weighted interventions in your office first to ensure the client only invests in items that benefit them. If a client is very sensory-seeking for weighted items, they might also enjoy engaging in a mindfulness exercise while lifting small hand weights (approximately one to three pounds). They can sit with the physical sensation of engaging their muscles and notice how this feels. While engaging in this exercise, you can also tap into some strengths-based work by observing how their body's strength literally carries weight.

WILBARGER BRUSHING PROTOCOL

ALL AGES

Sensory brushing, often known as the Wilbarger Brushing Protocol, is an intervention that clients can do in session and in between appointments as homework. The technique uses a tool called a sensory brush or therapy brush, which comes in different sizes and retails for approximately $4 to $20. To acclimate your client to the protocol, you can include one in your office for practice, letting the caregiver or guardian brush the client. You might also consider purchasing extra brushes that you can lend or give to clients who need one and cannot afford it.

The Wilbarger Brushing Protocol consists of a supportive person applying the brush firmly to the client's skin on various parts of the body, including the arms, legs, and back, and brushing back and forth. A parent, guardian, or loved one can administer the brushing protocol on a predetermined schedule. Typically, the protocol takes less than five minutes per sitting, but the time can be extended if the client enjoys the brushing sensation. It has been found to be a safe intervention for children of all ages and even infants!

Brushing protocols can help with a variety of concerns:

- Regular brushing can help reduce "defensive" responding to sensory experiences. In other words, the technique can help retrain brains that tend to overrespond to sensory experiences in ways that interfere with comfort, quality of life, and functioning.

- As this sensory defensiveness reduces, clients often report decreased anxiety, as they do not have to fear unexpected sensory input.

- Clients who are sensory-seeking and engage in stims that risk injury sometimes find that the brushing protocol replaces the harmful stim behavior in meeting their sensory needs.

- Brushing protocols can foster attachment and communication between the client and their caregiver.

- The brushing sensation can increase body awareness by drawing the client's attention to the feeling of the brush.

FINGER PAINTING

ALL AGES

Sensory-seeking individuals often enjoy activities that involve getting "mess" on their hands and arms. Finger painting taps into this sensory need and allows for creative expression in a safe, affirming environment. While you can encourage the client to consider a specific topic or prompt for their art, this activity lends itself well to a nondirective approach with an emphasis on the sensory process itself. Set up whatever covering, smock, or protective tarp is needed in order to let the client fully engage in the activity. If you are unable to sit with this process out of fear that the client will make a mess, the client may pick up on your hesitation and not get as much out of the activity.

The therapeutic benefit of creative expression rests in the process of creating rather than the outcome, so encourage your client to look past perceived mistakes (or sit with resulting feelings of discomfort) rather than trying to make the resulting image look a particular way. You can reinforce this concept by prefacing the activity with a discussion about what the client wants to do with their completed project, including the option to simply throw it away or destroy it. Of course, if the client wants to keep their art, this is appropriate as well, but for some, creating something with the intent of destroying it helps them get out of their own way with the process.

Clients who are anxious about how their art will turn out or who feel self-conscious about creating artwork in the session often benefit from the therapist joining them in this activity. This allows you to model self-acceptance and engagement without giving prompts or commands to the client.

SCULPTING

AGES 5+

Sculpting has similar sensory involvement to finger painting, but on a three-dimensional scale rather than two-dimensional. It taps into tactile sensory-seeking needs combined with creative expression. You can sculpt with clay that either air dries or can be fired in an oven or kiln (if you have the appropriate equipment available) if the client wants to be able to keep their creation. At the same time, if you are working on embracing the sensory experience of sculpting and letting go of a specific outcome, you might choose to use Play-Doh or reusable clay so you can destroy the sculptures at the end.

This activity has similar therapeutic and sensory benefits as finger painting but with a different medium and different tactile experience, so you and your client can choose the method that best fits their needs. Clay and paint (and different types of clay and paint) vary in texture, and clients will have individual preferences that they may not even be able to articulate. Let them try different methods for creative expression and determine when they have the most positive sensory experience.

In addition to texture, clients' visual sensory preferences can influence which intervention is most appropriate. Sculpting often involves only one color of clay, whereas painting can involve the full color spectrum.

SLIME

Some autistic people really enjoy the tactile sensation of making and playing with slime, so if you have the space and materials available, this activity can engage your client through a tactile sensory experience. Additionally, the act of making slime involves following specific steps, which can be beneficial to clients working on receptive communication, demand avoidance, and problem-solving.

Clients who are both sensory-seeking and sensory-avoidant around tactile experiences might benefit from creating different types of slime because various recipes yield different texture outcomes, and this can help the client explore what sensations they do and do not enjoy. Many slime recipes are available for free online.

Basic slime includes white glue, baking soda, and saline solution. Ingredient ratios, the local climate, and even the weather that day can impact how the slime comes out. If the slime is too runny, you likely need to add glue, and if it is too hard, you can add water to soften it. The following added ingredients can change the texture and visual appeal of the slime based on preference:

- **Air dry clay:** Makes the slime spreadable like butter and able to hold its shape if you sculpt with it

- **Shaving cream:** Makes the slime softer and fluffier

- **Lotion:** Makes the slime softer and, if scented, adds a smell

- **Food coloring:** Changes the color

- **Corn starch:** Makes the slime more stretchy

- **Glitter:** Adds sparkle, light, and a grainy texture

- **Small Styrofoam balls:** Adds a crunchy texture

- **Metallic paints:** Makes the slime shiny

- **Glow paint:** Makes the slime glow in the dark

Of course, you can always experiment with other options and ingredients to invent even more types of slime!

Interoception and Mindfulness Interventions

Interoception refers to our ability to recognize, sense, and respond to internal body sensations. As is the case with other sensory experiences, autistic people tend to experience interoception differently than nonautistic people. Some people are hyperaware of interoception, which leads to distress because they are more aware of things going on inside the body and might overrespond to benign changes, misinterpreting them as harmful. For example, people who experience panic attacks (particularly those with a diagnosable panic disorder) are often overly aware of internal changes and become worried that any physiological change could indicate an oncoming panic attack (Van Deist, 2019). This overanalysis of internal processes can unfortunately have the opposite of a protective effect and can actually be the trigger for a panic attack.

On the other hand, some autistic clients are hypoaware of interoceptive experiences, which can be equally problematic. Many autistic people struggle to recognize when they feel hungry, thirsty, or tired, or when they need to use the bathroom, especially when they are hyperfocused on a special interest. Not eating or drinking enough can be emotionally distressing and have medical consequences, and waiting too long to use the bathroom can cause urinary tract infections.

Atypical sensory processing may explain why autistic people experience interoception differently than nonautistic people. Additionally, traumatic experiences can lead autistic people to detach from their internal processes in a dissociative way. For them, it is unsafe to be aware of these internal processes because they can evoke trauma memories (Payne et al., 2015). As previously discussed, existing as an autistic person in this world can be stressful and traumatic, and autistic people are at higher risk for abuse and trauma. Autistic people are also at higher risk for chronic pain and other medical issues compared to nonautistic people. Those who experience chronic pain might be unable to cope with the full awareness of their internal painful sensations, leading them to detach as a way to cope with this.

In the following section, you'll find activities to build interoceptive awareness for clients whose disengagement from their internal processes causes problems in their functioning. It also includes activities to "turn off" that awareness for those who are overly focused on these experiences to their detriment. As always, collaborate with your client to determine what they find beneficial and what their needs are.

This section also includes mindfulness activities to enhance awareness of needs, sensations, and so forth. Many people find mindfulness activities relaxing, helpful, and regulating, but they are not a one-size-fits-all solution. As with all neurodiversity-affirming care, you must always be aware that a given client might not benefit from an intervention, even if you've had success using it with other clients. Some mindfulness-based interventions can even be harmful (Baer et al., 2021). For example, clients with chronic pain may experience increased pain levels in response to mindfulness interventions focused on body awareness. Clients who are prone to dissociation may also experience an exacerbation of symptoms in response to such interventions. Additionally, clients with a history of psychosis have been cautioned to only use mindfulness carefully and with adapted interventions to prevent harm (Chadwick, 2014).

If a client states that mindfulness was harmful to them in the past, you may be tempted to encourage them to try it again or reassure them that you do mindfulness differently. However, you must remember that there are people for whom mindfulness is not a good fit. Additionally, empowering clients in an affirming environment means listening to them. If a client is uncertain about trying mindfulness, you can choose different interventions. In short, use caution and listen to your clients. No intervention (or type of intervention) is going to help everyone. That is why we have so many options available.

STIM ON PURPOSE

AGES 8+

Many nonaffirming treatment approaches have taught autistic people that their stim behaviors are bad, are wrong, or should be suppressed. Even if an individual has not attended treatment, many autistic people are teased or bullied for stim behaviors and suppress them to avoid backlash from the people around them. As noted previously, it is not helpful to encourage an autistic person to hide nonharmful stims to avoid mistreatment because this sends the same message: that the stim is shameful or embarrassing. However, an individual may feel unsafe exhibiting a stim behavior in front of other people. Sometimes, masking behavior can be protective, and an autistic person who uses this behavior to avoid mistreatment is not doing anything wrong. Unfortunately, you cannot force other people in the client's life to be affirming.

At the same time, perpetual masking is exhausting and can lead to burnout in the long term. This is particularly the case for clients who have internalized shame or embarrassment about stim behaviors because of trauma or past mistreatment, who might not even feel comfortable stimming in private. You can help them safely process these feelings in treatment, and if they are open to it, they might benefit from practicing stims on purpose. The client can practice these stims in the office or wait until they get home if they are uncertain about even you seeing them stim.

The following list includes specific stims you can recommend based on the client's sensory needs. For example, if the client is sensory-seeking related to sound, they might want to listen to a song on repeat. If they prefer to move around, movement-based stims might be a better option for them. This list is not exhaustive but presents ideas to help clients identify which stims they prefer. Since some stims can be physically harmful, those presented here are intended as safe alternatives that a client can do without risking bodily harm or damage to property.

Movement Stims	
• Repeatedly moving or playing with a fidget item	• Rocking back and forth
• Twirling a pencil	• Tapping or jiggling your foot or leg
• Tapping your fingers	• Pacing
• Flapping your hands	• Blinking in a specific way
	• Sitting or standing in a specific posture

Sound Stims	
• Listening to a song on repeat	• Watching a video on repeat
Verbal Stims	
• Humming • Whistling	• Repeating a phrase from a preferred piece of media • Repeating an affirming quote
Tactile Stims	
• Rubbing a soft item • Touching an object with an interesting texture	• Picking at something that is safe to pick at • Petting an emotional support animal • Chewing on chewelry
Visual Stims	
• Watching a moving object	• Staring at a visually appealing object

The following *Stim Reflection Log* can help the client notice what stims they did and did not find helpful, but some might find this task overwhelming or simply tedious—an affirming therapist will recognize that tracking a stim's effectiveness is not the right fit for every client and will adjust accordingly.

Stim Reflection Log

Day and Time	Mood Before	Stim	Mood After

I CAN CHANGE HOW MY BODY FEELS

AGES 5+

For some autistic people, feelings get intense quickly, and they struggle to self-regulate when this happens. This intervention is designed to help them identify when physiological changes occur in the body that are indicative of an upcoming meltdown or shutdown. Since emotions can be tied to physiological responses (e.g., anxiety manifesting as increased heart rate), focusing on lowering those responses can help reduce big feelings. Although it is not possible to fully control every body function and response, the goal is for the client to recognize small ways that they can influence what their body is doing.

Before starting this activity, have the client identify a physical activity that they can comfortably and safely do in your office for 30 seconds to one minute (e.g., running in place, jumping jacks, pushups). Have them also choose a relaxation skill, stim behavior, or calming activity that they can do for about one minute. Then ask the client to check their pulse. They can use a smart device if they have one, or measure the pulse in their neck with a finger. Have them count their heartbeats for 10 seconds and multiply their count by six to get their current heart rate. If the client is able, have them also identify any emotions they are experiencing in the moment and describe how intense those emotions are.

Next, time the client while they do their chosen physical activity. Although this intervention works best if they can maintain the activity for at least 30 seconds, cut it short if they indicate they need or want to stop. Take their pulse again, and note it next to the original heart rate. Inquire about any changes to the client's emotional state.

Now, have the client engage in their relaxation, stim, or calming behavior, and time them for one minute before checking their heart rate for a third time. Also ask about their emotional state again. Most likely, the client's heart rate will increase when they engage in the physical activity and lower when they use a relaxation skill. This demonstrates in a physical, measurable way how choices can sometimes have an impact on internal functions and how these changes might impact how the client is feeling. Use this as a starting point for the client to develop a list of skills and tools that help them self-regulate during difficult moments.

Note: This activity is contraindicated if the client has a heart issue. Ask about this before trying this intervention. If the client begins to feel dizzy or lightheaded, stop. Remember to ensure that the client understands they can say no or discontinue an intervention if they become uncomfortable.

LISTEN TO YOUR HEART(BEAT)

AGES 4+

This activity is designed to help clients become more in touch with their internal body processes. Since heartbeat is relatively easy to measure, it is a simple way for clients to start to notice what is going on for them internally and to tap into their body's needs in the moment. If you have access to a stethoscope, you can take a literal approach to this activity. Invite the client to put the stethoscope on, unless the feeling of the stethoscope causes a sensory issue (make sure they know they can tell you this, and stop if they indicate they need to stop!), and listen to their own heartbeat in real time. If they have a device that can take their pulse, there are some free smartphone applications that can also play the sound of their heartbeat through the device's speaker.

If the client is comfortable, they can do a physical activity to raise their heart rate or a relaxation activity to slow it down and listen in real time as the speed of their heartbeat changes. This helps build their awareness of body sensations in a nonjudgmental way, as they are merely observing what their heart does without expectation.

BODY CLUES

AGES 8+

This is similar to the heartbeat activity but expands it to additional body sensations. The goal is for clients to identify different physiological responses they might experience and to become more consciously aware of when these sensations happen. This helps the client gain insight into their emotions as they connect their feelings to associated physiological responses, as well as needs like hunger, thirst, or urges to use the bathroom. Since many autistic people have different experiences of interoception, this can help them get back in touch with what their body is doing and what it needs.

Together with your client, make a list of different physiological experiences their body has. If the client is able, encourage them to share experiences they are familiar with. If they are unsure, you can start with this body sensations list:

- Heart beating faster
- Heart slowing down
- Muscles getting tense
- Muscles relaxing
- Headache or tension in the scalp
- Sweating
- Salivating
- Dry mouth
- Breathing faster

- Breathing slowing down
- Shivering
- Dizziness
- Eyes going wide
- Squinting
- Shaking
- Nausea or stomachache
- Aching joints

If the client is able, have them identify a time when they have felt these different internal experiences. If relevant, they can share emotions connected with each sensation or experience. If a client struggles to identify any emotions, focus instead on what was going on inside of their body at the time: Did this situation make their muscles feel tense? Did their heart beat faster? Did they experience any discomfort or pain in their body? Even if the client struggles to name the specific emotion tied to the triggering event, they can develop insight into physiological body cues that can indicate they are having trouble.

SLOWING MY BODY DOWN

AGES 8+

This activity uses the same body sensations list from the previous *Body Clues* activity. Take the list, including any additional sensations your client has experienced, and divide it into three categories: indications that their body is speeding up (e.g., heart beating faster), indications that their body is slowing down (e.g., muscles relaxing), and any sensations that they feel do not fit into the other two categories. Use the following *What Do My Body Sensations Mean?* worksheet to track the client's responses.

Again, this activity helps clients identify when their feelings are getting bigger or smaller (i.e., when they might be escalating or calming down). This information can help them learn to notice if they need to take a break, leave a space, or ask for help from a loved one. By putting the focus on objective body experiences, the client does not have to figure out what specific emotion they are experiencing. They can simply observe what their body is doing and take appropriate action.

What Do My Body Sensations Mean?

I Am Speeding Up	I Am Slowing Down	Neither

FIND YOUR BREATH

ALL AGES

This breathing exercise is intended to increase awareness of the breath, which can help clients take deep, calming breaths and be aware of changes to their breathing that may indicate that they are having an emotional response they need to address. Remember, though, that for some clients, being prompted to breathe or take big breaths can be a trigger. They may have a history of condescendingly being told to breathe when they are escalated or having a meltdown. In addition, abusers might have told them to breathe during or after abusive behavior. Therefore, it is important to ask clients about any triggers associated with breathing before doing this intervention.

Note, too, that not everyone is aware of what their triggers are, especially if they have not previously had a safe space to acknowledge them. Even if a client indicates that they are comfortable with breathing exercises, make sure they understand that they can change their mind at any time during this activity and their needs will be honored. Additionally, if you notice that the client is tensing up or becoming agitated, discontinue the activity, as the client might not realize they are escalating right away, or they might not feel safe indicating that they want to stop even if you have told them they are allowed to do so.

If the client is able to engage in breathing activities, have them find a comfortable position. Together, take a few slow, deep breaths in and out. Try to make each breath slightly deeper than the last one. Ask them to notice where they most feel the breath in their body: in their shoulders, chest, stomach, or somewhere else? With your client, see if you can change where the focus of the breath goes (like shifting from the shoulders to the stomach) and see if this affects how deeply you and your client are able to breathe. You can also have the client practice just noticing where their breath is falling in a given moment. This can help improve self-regulation and cue relaxation behaviors to prevent escalation.

FIVE SENSES GAME

AGES 5+

If a client is working on building greater sensory awareness but struggles with interoception, this game can help them bring attention to their experience with an emphasis on what is happening in their environment rather than what is going on inside of their bodies. For clients who are not ready to explore internal cues, or for those with chronic pain who struggle with those activities as a result, this can be a good alternative.

For this game, you just ask the client to tune into the five senses: sight, sound, touch, smell, and taste. To keep things simple, ask your client to identify in this moment:

1. What do you see?
2. What do you hear?
3. What do you feel?
4. What do you smell?
5. What do you taste?

Note that, if the client is not presently eating or drinking anything in session, they might state that they do not taste anything. Depending on the client, you can make a judgment call about whether to have them sit with their sense of taste and see if they can identify anything, or simply move on.

PHYSICAL GROUNDING

AGES 8+

Physical grounding involves engaging your senses and using your body to bring your awareness to the present moment while letting go of any thoughts, feelings, or sensations that are troubling. As with the previous *Five Senses Game*, this process can help clients focus their attention on what is happening in the here and now without having to bring further awareness to internal processes. Physical grounding has been found beneficial for those with chronic pain issues who are trying to stay present in the moment while detaching from their body's pain.

It can help to explain the concept of physical grounding to the client and offer multiple activities they can try, including inviting them to suggest their own techniques. Physical grounding can take many different forms, but if the client wants suggestions, you can offer some of the following:

- Hold an ice cube in your hand and focus on the cold feeling.
- Stretch and really focus on how each muscle feels as you stretch it.
- Walk slowly in a circle, noticing your body's weight on each foot as you move.
- Touch an object and describe its texture in extreme detail.
- Look at an object and describe its appearance in extreme detail.
- Eat a mint or another candy with a strong flavor and describe the flavors in detail.
- Do a breathing exercise.
- Describe your physical environment in extreme detail.
- Smell something with a strong scent, like essential oils or perfume, and try to really notice the smell.
- Do movement-based stims.

MENTAL GROUNDING

AGES 8+

Mental grounding has the same therapeutic benefits as physical grounding, without the physical component. It involves bringing yourself into the present moment through thoughts and language rather than a physical sensory experience. Clients who are uncomfortable with physical activities or whose medical conditions make those exercises challenging or impossible may benefit from mental grounding.

Once again, clients may indicate their comfort with or preference for a specific mental grounding activity, but you may use the following as examples or starting points:

- Say the alphabet backward.

- Count to 100 by sevens.

- Describing an event in great detail: Think of a memory that is soothing to you and describe it in as much detail as you can, being as specific as possible.

- Guided imagery: Use a preferred meditation script that involves visualization (if the client is able to visualize images in their mind).

- The categories game: Choose a category and think of as many things that fit into that category as you can. Try to think of at least 10 items and go for more if possible. Examples of categories might include breeds of a certain animal, characters in a television show, or books by a certain author.

- Repeat a phrase: Choose a word, phrase, or quote that you find soothing, and repeat it several times.

- Plan something fun: Think about something you will be able to do in the future and make plans in your mind of how you want that to go. For example, you can think about what you want to do on an upcoming vacation or make plans to treat yourself later.

- Imagine a loved one: Imagine a conversation with someone you care about, whose presence is soothing to you. What would they say to you right now, and how would you respond?

WHERE DO YOU FEEL THAT?

AGES 4+

Since it is important to understand your client's emotional experience, but some autistic people struggle to identify and articulate their emotions, you must understand alternative ways to communicate and understand what your clients are communicating to you. If a client is able to identify and express different body sensations, they might be able to provide insight into their emotional state by indicating where in their body they experience a feeling, and how that feeling manifests as a body sensation.

For this activity, the client will start by simply identifying what part of their body is experiencing a feeling (e.g., their chest) and later build on that to identify specific body sensations they are experiencing (e.g., increased heart rate). Ask the client to record their responses using the following body outline. This starting point opens the door for you to explore together whether the feeling is pleasant or unpleasant, what (if any) environmental factor triggered the feeling, and what causes the feeling to get bigger or smaller. All of this can be done without having to name the feeling, which can allow clients who struggle with that particular skill to effectively express themselves anyway.

Body Outline

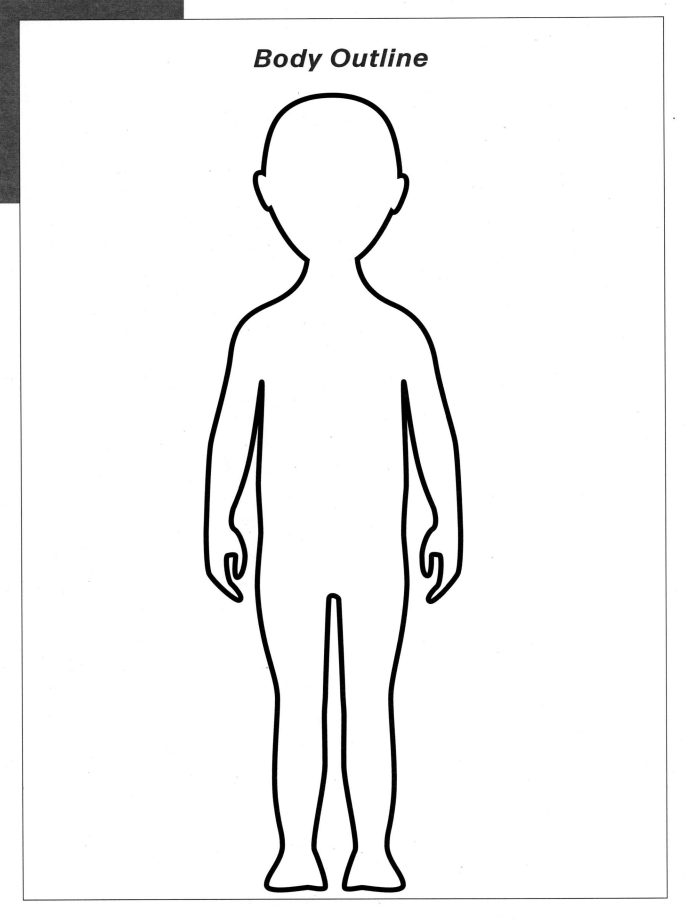

HOW DO EMOTIONS FEEL IN MY BODY?

AGES 8+

This activity builds on the last one by helping clients identify the specific feelings associated with different body sensations. This helps them better understand their own emotional experiences and allows loved ones to more easily understand their needs. Use the *Body Clues* activity from page 100 to help the client link different sensations to different parts of their body. Have them make a list of different emotions, and note which body sensations tend to occur with each emotion. A sample list of emotions can include:

- Happy
- Sad
- Angry
- Scared
- Excited
- Disappointed
- Calm
- Agitated
- Distraught
- Defensive
- Embarrassed
- Relieved

- Lonely
- Hopeless
- Dreading
- Affectionate
- Confident
- Capable
- Numb
- Anxious
- Stubborn
- Lonely
- Withdrawn
- Enraged

- Annoyed
- Rushed
- Overwhelmed
- Restless
- Surprised
- Bored
- Apathetic
- Guilty
- Ashamed
- Vulnerable
- Grateful

As the client learns to identify where they experience different emotions in their body, they can start to recognize feelings in real time. They can then recognize feelings when they are less intense and take steps to alleviate distress before a meltdown, shutdown, or outburst. When recognizing the intensity of feelings, many therapy interventions use a 10-point Likert scale, with 1 being "not feeling this emotion at all" and 10 being "the most intensely I have ever felt this emotion." While this can be a helpful tool for some, autistic clients who have a strong need for precision may struggle with the 1–10 scale. For these clients, a 1–100 scale can allow for more specificity. At the same time, clients who become overwhelmed by too many choices may prefer a simpler 1–5 scale. Let them choose what works best for them.

If the client is open to it, have them practice checking in on their body sensations, associated emotions, and emotional intensity in between sessions using the following *My Body Sensations Tracker* log. This can help them get in the habit of automatically noticing their feelings, identifying specific triggers for these feelings, and using coping skills to regulate if need be. If the client lives with a guardian or caretaker, encourage all household members to practice this activity, which normalizes the behavior and can help the client feel more comfortable so they are not singled out. It can also improve communication and enhance the caregiver's regulation skills. After all, we can all benefit from expressing our feelings clearly!

My Body Sensations Tracker

Date and Time	Body Sensation(s)	Emotion (if any)	Intensity	Environmental Triggers	Coping Skill

MIRRORING ACTIVITY

AGES 6+

Mirroring is the act of imitating another person's behaviors, movements, expressions, or gestures. Some people unintentionally engage in mirroring behavior, including some autistic people, but it's also possible to practice intentional mirroring to build and teach certain skills. For example, you can mirror facial expressions to educate the client about how different emotions might look, which can help them learn to recognize what others are feeling. Similarly, you can mirror movements associated with different emotional states (e.g., slumped posture for sadness) to build greater emotional awareness. Mirroring can also be helpful in building communication skills. While it is not appropriate to teach an autistic person that their natural communication preferences are wrong or bad, they may nonetheless benefit from learning about other forms of communication so they can better navigate interactions and maintain safety.

When working on a specific skill, you can simply model the skill while the client copies your movements as closely as possible. If a client struggles with mirroring due to difficulty following "instructions," you can make the activity into a game where you take turns mirroring each other. This gives the autistic person control over the activity and puts them in charge when it is your turn to mirror them.

BODY SCAN

AGES 8+

You may be familiar with body scan activities, which usually consist of a mindful awareness script in which you cue the client to check in with each part of their body, either from the top of their head to the bottoms of their feet or vice versa. This activity can make clients aware of any tension in their body or any body clues they had not previously noticed. However, this activity can be triggering for some clients, such as those with chronic pain issues or certain trauma symptoms, so check in with your client and only do this activity if they are comfortable. Additionally, if you try the activity and the client has a negative experience, discontinue it right away.

Many body scan scripts already exist in different books and on the internet. Since clients have different preferences (and those with trauma history may have specific triggers), it can be helpful to create a body scan script together. You can use this outline as a starting point:

1. Start with a call to bring attention to this moment and to settle the body.

2. Invite the client to engage in a self-regulation skill. (Often, scripts focus on deep breathing here, which is certainly appropriate as long as the client is comfortable with that.)

3. Cue the client to check in with different parts of the body, usually traveling either up or down, with notes to pause and focus on specific areas. Usually this includes the head, shoulders, arms, torso, legs, and feet, but let the client decide what they want to focus on.

4. Ask the client to make note of specific sensations they observe during the activity (e.g., tension or stress), and encourage them to observe these experiences without judgment.

5. Cue the body to let go of anything not serving it, like tension or another unpleasant feeling.

6. Help the client center themselves and shift out of the exercise.

The client can take the script with them to do this activity on their own or with a caregiver. In the session, you can follow the script together or take turns reading it to each other to alternate who does the body scan. If the client is open to sharing, you can ask them about their experience and what they noticed while engaging in the activity. You can even start or end each session with a body scan as a transition activity.

MUSCLE RELAXATION

This activity is similar to the previous body scan, but it cues the client to take a specific action to reduce tension in their body rather than simply observing what comes up. In particular, this exercise consists of scanning various parts of the body and intentionally squeezing and then releasing different muscle groups. It can help ease tension and bring down intense emotions as a result.

You can find many progressive muscle relaxation scripts online or from other resources, but clients might benefit from creating their own relaxation script to enhance their engagement in the activity and to ensure that there are no accidental triggers. You and your client can create a custom muscle relaxation script from the following outline:

1. Start with a call to bring attention to this moment and to settle the body.

2. Invite the client to engage in a self-regulation skill, either deep breathing or something else that they prefer.

3. Cue the client to tense muscles in various parts of their body (usually from the top down or bottom up), squeezing the muscles as tightly as they can before mindfully and intentionally releasing them. Let the client decide which muscles they want to include or exclude as part of this step.

4. After each muscle group, encourage the client to take a moment to experience the feeling of relief and relaxation.

5. After completing the last muscle group, help the client center themselves and shift out of the exercise.

WHAT DOES MY BODY NEED?

AGES 5+

As clients develop insight into what is going on in their bodies, they can better express their emotional and physical needs and get those needs met. Using the record sheets from previous activities, clients can deliberately check in with their bodies on a regular basis to determine what their needs are in a given moment. They can either set an alarm or ask their caregiver to remind them to complete these scheduled check-ins. If there are specific body needs that the client tends to overlook or forget about, make a list together so they can deliberately check in on each of these needs. For example, a client who forgets to take meal breaks can check in on their hunger cues. Or if a client finds the body scan activity beneficial, encourage them to use this particular kind of script to notice different body needs.

Additionally, if a client has ongoing difficulty with interoception, have them schedule times to get their needs met whether they feel a body cue or not. For example, a client who does not notice when they feel hungry might commit to eating every day at 1 p.m. regardless of whether they notice a body cue, or a client who does not realize they need to use the bathroom can set an alarm to stop what they are doing and attempt to go to the bathroom every two hours while they are awake.

SILENCING THE INNER CRITIC

AGES 8+

Although thinking is a process that often feels deliberate, we constantly have thoughts we do not mean to have or that we do not truly believe. The negative self-thoughts that autistic clients have may be informed by criticism or emotional abuse they have experienced in the past. These negative, internalized thoughts represent the inner critic.

By processing their thoughts and emotions in therapy, clients may begin to realize that many of these thoughts are cruel and hurtful. However, coming to this realization is only the first step. When clients begin countering negative thoughts, they are met with a new challenge: They often begin arguing with themselves, leading to a cycle of additional negative thoughts. It might go something like this: "Oh no, I'm thinking negatively about myself again when I am trying so hard not to do that. I'm so bad at this. I can't even have positive thoughts! Stop being so mean to yourself! Why are you so terrible at everything?"

If clients learn to think of their inner critic as an entity separate from themselves, they can shift this conversation. Although the inner critic is not *literally* another entity, they can personify it as such. If they think of those negative thoughts as someone other than themselves, they can shut down any negative self-talk without creating additional negative thoughts. Clients can name their inner critic and even make a picture of the critic if they are so inclined. They can then practice telling their inner critic to leave them alone, go away, or even "shut up!"

MINDFUL WRITING

AGES 8+

For clients who struggle with recognizing their emotions, journaling interventions can help them process what is happening for them in real time. Clients who enjoy writing may benefit from this kind of intervention to center themselves and bring their attention to their current emotional state. Specific prompts that can help clients with this activity include:

1. **Set an intention.** The client can write down their needs and intentions for the current moment. It can be helpful to do this first thing in the morning as they prepare for their day.

2. **Free write any feelings.** The client can take a preset amount of time (often 5 to 10 minutes is sufficient for this) to write whatever comes to their mind without judgment. They can complete this at a set time each day or when they feel escalated. It can be helpful to review and process these writings in session, if the client is comfortable with this.

3. **Do a written body scan.** Rather than reading or listening to a body scan script, the client can write down sensations they feel in each section of their body. This can help clients who prefer not to sit still with a body scan or who want to track their body sensations in more depth to look for patterns or triggers.

Food-Based Interventions

Many autistic people experience food-related issues, including "pickiness" due to severe sensory issues, eating disorders, or medical issues that cause food sensitivities and digestive distress. If a client has a history of being forced to eat certain foods, they might have additional issues and stress around food and eating, including a strong need to control the things they eat.

In the following section, you will find several interventions to help clients work through food concerns or eating-related stress. I would like to issue a special thank-you to Matthew Broberg-Moffitt, author of *Color Taste Texture* and expert on food and eating issues, who allowed me to ask questions about appropriate interventions and approaches to address this issue. When using these interventions with clients, remember to know the limitations of your scope, training, and competency. If you do not have training as a nutritionist, know when to refer clients to someone who can help with this aspect of their diet. At the same time, you can use the educational materials and therapeutic interventions in this section to help clients confront and improve their relationship with food, as well as help caregivers avoid creating stress and trauma around food.

When clients are not eating enough or getting proper nutrition, it can significantly impact their physical health and mental health. If you have concerns around food and eating, immediately make sure your client gets medical attention from a physician. Additionally, ensure that medical causes for food sensitivities (such as allergies, digestive issues, or other sensitivities) are either ruled out or treated first and foremost.

Education for Caregivers

Just as many people have limited information about autism and the autistic community, there exists a wealth of misinformation around food and eating, especially for parents. Even many mental health professionals are taught that "When they get hungry enough, they will eat." Autistic clients with sensory issues around eating and food aversions will, in fact, *not* just eat when they get hungry, and this approach can cause harm. Since education is vital in offering affirming care and support, here are tips and educational information to give to caregivers whose autistic loved ones are struggling with food and eating.

Sample Script

Many autistic people experience issues around food and eating, which nonautistic caregivers often misinterpret as "pickiness" or "resistance." You may feel frustrated, worried, or uncertain what you can do to ensure your child or loved one receives appropriate nourishment. Here are some key steps you can take to provide affirming care and support.

Don't force feed. It can be frustrating when your child or loved one is not eating. You might even feel like they are "refusing" to eat, even though food aversion is about being unable to eat rather than refusing to eat. It can be tempting to get into a power struggle and attempt to force your child to eat, but this does not help anyone. In fact, this can be traumatic and can cause more severe food issues. Your child might resist eating in order to regain a sense of control after being forced to eat, or they might associate mealtimes with the stress and trauma of being forced to eat. Take a breath, and remember they are not trying to be difficult but rather are communicating their needs in the moment.

Calmly seek feedback. When your child or loved one indicates that they do not want to eat something presented to them, you can ask them if there is something specific about the food that they dislike. Is it the texture or taste? Is it the appearance or color? Does the food contain an ingredient that they know will not make them feel good? Make sure you are calm, and make it clear that you are seeking feedback to determine alternative foods that they will feel comfortable eating. You are not debating them or trying to convince them to eat—you are trying to help.

Don't get defensive. It is easy to take it personally when someone declines to eat food that you prepared for them. If your child or loved one indicates that they cannot eat food that you prepared, remember that they are trusting you by expressing a need because they believe you will support them and help them. It is not a reflection of your cooking skills!

Never trick them. You might truly believe that your child or loved one would enjoy certain foods "if they would just try it." You might be tempted to sneak ingredients into their meals to "prove" that they do not actually dislike that food. You may even be concerned that they are not getting proper nutrition and feel like sneaking these ingredients is the only way to ensure they are consuming a healthy diet. Regardless of your intentions, deceit and trickery shatter trust. If your child does not want to eat a certain food because it is making them feel sick, they might not have the language or insight to express that to you. Sneaking in those ingredients can physically harm them if this is the case. Even if the food is not making them physically sick, this behavior will guarantee that they will never trust you with anything again if they find out. And autistic people with sensory issues often catch on because they can tell the difference when you interfere with their food.

Don't judge them. Again, your child or loved one is not trying to be difficult or cause problems by "refusing" to eat certain foods. By judging them for their food needs, you risk creating an inner critic who shames them for having needs. This can cause them to ignore these needs, leading them to eat foods that cause them discomfort or that harm them in order to be "good" or gain approval.

Remember that all food is good food. Society constantly inundates us with diet culture and the idea that we must eat "good" foods and avoid "bad" foods. But assigning moral value to food is harmful and often inaccurate. "Good" food is food that serves you physically, psychologically, and emotionally. It can be difficult to let go of your preconceived ideas about "good" food, but this can help reduce shame around food sensitivities and aversions.

Ask for help if you need to. If you are worried about your child or loved one getting sufficient nutrition, get a referral to a nutritionist or physician to check on their well-being and ensure that they are healthy. A nutritionist can provide feedback and suggestions for getting proper nutrition while coping with food aversions.

Communicate expectations to other important people. Just like it might be difficult for you to understand that your child or loved one's food aversions are real and valid, others in their life might not realize this. Grandparents or other significant adults in their life might want to sneak unsafe foods, refuse to accommodate food needs, or pressure your child to eat specific foods. Make your expectations clear, and if someone refuses to ensure that your child's needs are met safely, do not allow that person to be in control of anything your child eats.

Let your loved one know you're in their corner. You might not be able to get in front of every situation where your child might have a negative experience around food and eating, but you can communicate to them that you have their back and support their needs. Make sure your child knows that if someone goes against their food needs, this was done without your consent, and you will take steps to keep them safe in the future.

Remember that food aversion serves an important biological purpose. Humans (and most animals) are primed to develop aversions to certain foods for safety reasons. Have you ever had food poisoning, and afterward you could not eat that particular food without feeling sick? This happens for a reason! Your body linked that food to an illness and is now warning you not to consume that food again for fear of getting sick. This is a survival response. Since some autistic people are more sensitive to their environment, they are more likely to notice subtle body changes after eating, which can lead to limited food preferences in an effort to keep their body physically healthy. Any trait can cause problems when taken to an extreme, and this is a prime example. When food preferences get limited too much, the individual can become malnourished and unwell, which is the opposite of what their brain is trying to do by protecting them from potentially unsafe foods. Being aware of this process and its biological basis can help you be patient with an individual experiencing food aversions.

MINDFUL EATING

Mindful eating is the act of bringing your full attention to the experience of eating. Since eating a preferred food can be a stim behavior, this activity can help autistic people self-regulate. It can also help build insight when determining what foods cause different body feelings or medical responses.

To practice mindful eating, clients can simply center themselves and bring their full awareness to the present moment before having a snack or meal, or they can engage in a mindfulness script to fully experience a single bite or piece of food. (Some providers who use mindful eating in their practice keep candies or raisins in their office for this purpose. Of course, confirm any sensitivities or allergies before providing food for a client.) If you decide to engage in a mindful eating practice in session, you and your client can craft a script together that fits the client's needs and preferences:

1. Start by bringing the client's attention to the current moment and inviting them to set an intention for the activity.

2. Help the client center themselves, possibly with a breathing activity.

3. Guide the client in taking a moment to focus on the food, possibly taking in its appearance or scent.

4. Invite the client to slowly and intentionally consume the food, focusing on the taste.

5. After the client swallows, ask them to focus on the experience of taking in the food.

6. If appropriate, ask the client to take a moment to express gratitude to their body.

FED IS BEST—AT EVERY AGE

ALL AGES

When new parents are making decisions about bottle feeding versus breastfeeding or chestfeeding, they often struggle with determining the "best" option, and those who struggle with lactation might experience guilt about being unable to feed their baby in the "best" way. This has led to the idea that "fed is best"—in other words, that the "best" way to feed your child is whatever way ends in them having a full belly.

But this is not just true for infants! If an autistic person struggles with food aversions or sensitivities, it is most important to ensure they consume sufficient calories and nutrients, not to make sure they eat the "right" or "best" foods. We constantly internalize messages about the food we eat, including the concept that some food is morally or ethically superior to others, and the same holds true for autistic clients. Reframing this concept is a first step in addressing food aversions and helping clients and their guardians adjust expectations around foods to reduce eating-related stress. Since this stress can become a vicious cycle (e.g., food aversion leads to more stress around eating, which can intensify the aversions), this step back can be a good starting point for reducing that distress.

If a client is very young, you can engage in a discussion about "fed is best" with the caregiver, but if a client is old enough to understand the concept, you can certainly engage with them directly.

MY SAME FOODS

ALL AGES

In the autistic community, "same foods" refers to foods that an individual can eat repeatedly, on a daily basis or even for multiple meals per day. This can be comforting to the autistic person because they can incorporate specific foods into their routine and know what to expect from food on a given day. Same foods are often prepared in a specific way and using the exact same ingredients, including the same brand. For example, many autistic people have chicken nuggets as a same food, but not just any chicken nugget will do—their same food is one brand of chicken nugget that is prepared and consumed in a particular way.

Caregivers often become frustrated by same foods because they want their loved one to eat a varied diet. But remember, as long as the individual has sufficient calorie intake and appropriate nutrition, there is nothing inherently bad or wrong about eating the same thing over and over. In fact, this makes meal planning easy! Additionally, those who have food sensitivities might rely on same foods because they know how the food will make them feel physically.

Have clients compile a list of same foods that they feel comfortable eating, including specifics about how the food is prepared, brand names, and so forth. Caregivers can use this list to educate others about what their loved one can eat. Note that same foods can change over time. Like anyone, an autistic person's preferences and tastes can change. If a client has same foods that they rely on, it can help to review the same food list every six months or so to ensure it is accurate and up to date.

MY SAFE FOODS

ALL AGES

In the autistic community, "safe foods" refers to foods that bring comfort, help with self-regulation, or instill feelings of happiness or calm when eaten. Safe foods may also be same foods, but this is not a requirement. An autistic person might eat a same food every day but get particular enjoyment out of a different safe food.

The media often depicts things like chicken nuggets and french fries as safe foods, and while those may be some autistic people's safe foods, a safe food can be anything. Some autistic people have salad, pasta, or sushi as their safe food. While specific preferences vary, for many autistic people, a safe food is a specific brand and type of food. For example, they may have a specific order from a local restaurant that they order over and over again. Whenever possible, having a safe food available can be an easy way to help the autistic person manage sensory issues or overwhelm.

Similar to the previous activity, work with your client or their caregiver to make a list of safe foods that can help with regulation and coping. Again, updating this list on a regular basis can ensure accuracy and reflect any changes in the client's preferences and needs.

TRUST YOUR BODY: YOU KNOW YOUR LIMITS

AGES 6+

Many autistic people have been forced to eat foods they are uncomfortable with or that make them feel sick, leading them to question or disengage from their body's needs. The goal of this intervention is to teach the client to recognize their body's needs and limitations, to express these needs in a way the caregiver can understand, and to have those needs met in response to this communication. Once the client begins to recognize what their needs are, they can learn what foods serve their body, both physically and psychologically.

It is important to be aware that a client might exhibit stronger food aversions at first as they begin to recognize the ways in which they have pushed themselves too far in the past. This is normal and expected. As the client learns their limitations, they can then start to explore what additional foods might be safe for them. The process can look like this:

1. If applicable, educate the caregiver about interoception and how many autistic people disengage from their body's needs when these needs are not met.

2. Educate the client about this concept as well, and use appropriate mindfulness and interoception techniques to improve the client's ability to recognize what their needs are.

3. Make a plan for the client to let their caregiver know when a food is not working for them. This communication can simply be an indication that they do not want to eat the food. It is vital that the caregiver accepts the client's boundary and does not pressure them to "just try it" or "have a little bit," as this can be counterproductive for building trust. The caregiver should positively reinforce the client's communication of their needs, including thanking them for expressing themselves.

4. If the client is able, have them track what foods serve their body positively. If they are not able to do this, the caregiver can help with this process.

5. Use this information to determine what foods might be similar to foods the client is able to eat. *Only when the client is ready,* introduce alternatives. Once again, do not force the client to try anything they are not ready for or that they indicate they will not be able to safely eat.

The caregiver or guardian needs to be on board with this work. It is not helpful for the therapist to help the client get in touch with their body's needs if they leave the office and are forced to neglect these needs the rest of the time. Use the educational information at the beginning of this chapter to get the caregiver on board with this.

WHAT FOODS ARE SIMILAR TO WHAT YOU LIKE?

AGES 6+

Building off the last few activities, clients can use information about their safe foods and same foods (as well as the understanding that they have body autonomy) to widen their diet. Note that this is not always essential! It is okay to eat the same thing and only have a small variety of foods in one's diet, as long as those options are accessible, are sustainable, and provide adequate calories and nutrition. (As always, consult a qualified nutritionist and medical providers in determining when this need is met.) However, if the client is struggling to consume enough calories or showing evidence of malnourishment due to food aversions, they might benefit from expanding their food intake.

Using their safe food and same food lists, explore with your client what they enjoy about those particular foods. Is it the texture or flavor? Is it the seasoning? Is it the color or appearance? Using that information, identify foods that are similar but not identical to the same food or safe food. Make a list of similar foods that the client feels comfortable trying to incorporate into their diet. For example, they might feel comfortable trying a different brand of a safe food, foods that are the same color as the safe food, or foods with similar flavors or textures. The client should be actively involved in making this list to ensure that they are comfortable with the choices included.

Note that it is essential that the client take the lead with this activity. They should not be pressured into trying something with which they are not comfortable, as this can reinforce the biological drive to avoid foods perceived as unsafe and create stress and trauma around food and eating.

TRIAL AND ERROR

AGES 6+

Building on the previous activity, have the client begin experimenting with foods similar to their same and safe foods. Prepare them and their caregiver for the possibility that they will like some and dislike others, and this is okay. The client and their caregiver should both understand that the client's experience is most important, and only they can determine which foods serve them and which do not. When the client knows that they have control, they are more likely to try different foods because they know they can stop or backtrack as needed.

If the client prefers structure and wants to know what to expect, make a calendar together that describes what foods they will try and when. Have them track their responses both to the foods they like and those they dislike, as this can inform additional suggestions for other foods to try. Over time, this activity will help the client expand their food preferences to meet their nutritional needs without causing unnecessary stress or additional trauma. Instead, the client will be affirmed and empowered in making their own food choices.

THANK YOU, BRAIN!

ALL AGES

As noted earlier, our ability to develop food aversions is based on a biological need to identify when food might not be safe for consumption. When this need goes into overdrive, we can become averse to most foods and struggle to eat enough to sustain us. It can be tempting to fight against this drive and try to force ourselves (or force a loved one with food aversions) to eat, but this is counterproductive.

When your client experiences a food aversion, prompt them to pause and notice this feeling. (If appropriate, you can bring a food to the session that elicits aversion—with the understanding that the client will not eat the food but will instead demonstrate this biological response.) Remind the client that the feeling of aversion is their body cuing them that the food might not be safe, even if this thought might not be accurate.

Have your client make a statement of gratitude to their brain for wanting to keep them safe. They can also list other things their brain does to keep them safe. The statement might include things like "I'm grateful that my brain warns me when something might not be safe to eat" or "I'm glad for the times that my brain kept me safe by letting me know I might be in danger." This reframe can reduce stress responses to feelings of aversion to food.

Do this activity in conjunction with the caregiver or parent to ensure that the parent also understands how this reframe can reduce anxiety around food and eating. Use the scripts from the beginning of the chapter as needed to reinforce why it is counterproductive and harmful to force or pressure clients to eat foods that do not feel safe.

WHEN YOUR BODY FEELS HUNGRY

AGES 8+

Reduced interoception can make it difficult to recognize body needs, including hunger. Just like clients can learn to identify when their body is experiencing an emotion, they can learn to better recognize and respond to cues for hunger. Using the body sensations list from the *Body Clues* activity on page 100, as well as any additional body sensations you compiled in conjunction with your client, explore what the client's body feels like when they are experiencing hunger. For example, a client might notice sensations in their stomach or head when they start to feel hungry but have not connected these sensations to hunger. The client can then use the following body outline to communicate what sensations they experience in their body when they are hungry.

In addition to physiological responses, you can also ask the client to note any emotions that come up when they are hungry. For example, does the client tend to become cranky and irritable before they realize they have not eaten for a while? Note this! Emotions can serve as hunger cues just as physiological responses can. This can help the client recognize when they need to pause an activity in order to eat. As the client develops greater awareness of internal hunger cues, they may benefit from scheduling breaks specifically to eat. For instance, they can set alarms to pause and have a snack every few hours or schedule reminders for meals.

Body Outline

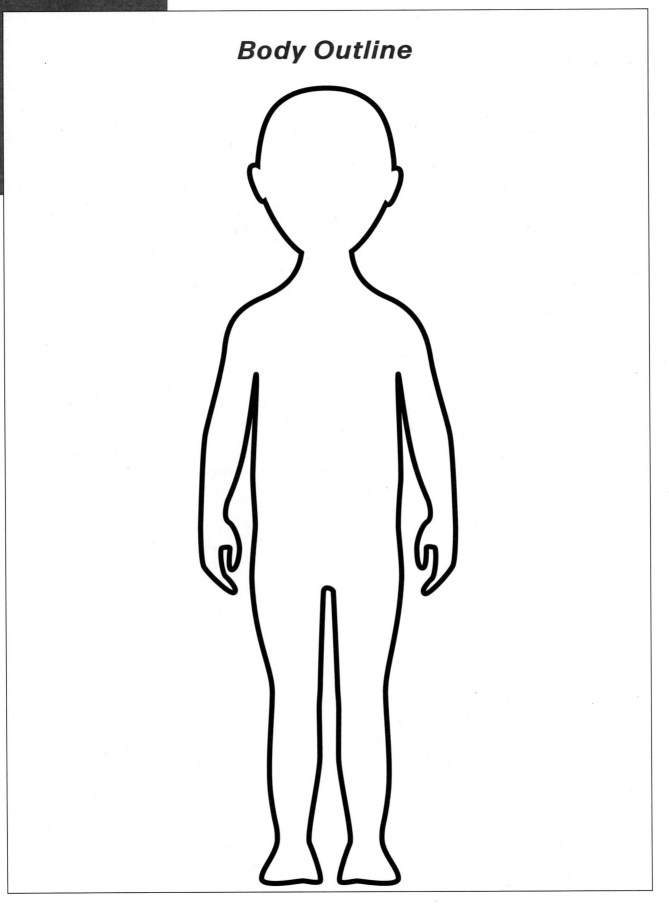

Demand Avoidance/Drive for Autonomy Interventions

While not formally recognized in the *DSM*, pathological demand avoidance, also known as PDA, is recognized within autism research as a "profile" with which autistic people can present. It is defined as a set of behaviors where the individual avoids anything perceived as a demand, such as refusing to complete tasks asked of them by a caregiver.

As is evident from the definition, PDA is not a neurodiversity-affirming term. While it is accurate that some autistic people struggle with responding to perceived demands, this definition focuses on PDA behaviors and how the autistic person impacts the people around them rather than determining what their needs are. Additionally, the so-called oppositional nature behind the disorder is not always accurate. For example, the need to push back against authority can manifest as a desire to work hard to accomplish something that someone has said is "impossible," so those with a PDA profile often accomplish quite a bit as a result of these traits.

Many autistic people are also inaccurately categorized as oppositional due to simple miscommunication. For instance, a teacher might give feedback on a child's assignment that asks, "Is there another way to solve this problem?" An autistic child might respond, "Yes, probably," and think they are done. The teacher could label this as rude or defiant because "They know what I was really asking," when, in fact, the child is now confused as to why they are in trouble. They answered the question, after all.

For this reason, some in the autistic and neurodiversity-affirming communities have moved to change the definition of PDA from pathological demand avoidance to persistent drive for autonomy. Essentially, PDA as a drive for autonomy refers to the individual's internal need to have control over their life, environment, and behavior by pushing back against perceived impositions on their autonomy from those around them. When providers conceptualize autistic PDA from this perspective, they recognize the individual's strength and drive rather than pathologizing a desire for empowerment as "bad" or "wrong."

With child clients especially, we often forget that autonomy is healthy and important for development. Unfortunately, many still cling to the idea that "good" children are compliant and do what adults tell them without question. However, it is essential to remember that we are not raising children to be obedient at all times; we are raising them to be functional adults. Children who are taught that they do not have the right to stand up for themselves are at risk for abuse and exploitation, and they grow into adults who do not know how to make decisions for themselves.

As a result, as with other autistic traits and profiles, while we recognize that there is not anything inherently bad with seeking autonomy, affirming providers also recognize that these tendencies can cause conflict and other issues in certain settings or when taken to an extreme. In turn, this section presents techniques for fostering effective communication and managing an individual's need for control and autonomy in healthy ways.

EDUCATION FOR CAREGIVERS

ALL AGES

Caregivers understandably become frustrated when faced with demand avoidance/drive for autonomy. Many parents in particular continue to adhere to the belief that children must be "obedient," and anything else is a sign of poor parenting. Even with a neurodiversity-affirming understanding of PDA behaviors, pushback and power struggles can be challenging. While education cannot fully alleviate frustration, it can go a long way in adjusting caregiver expectations and create a starting point for healthy, productive communication and support. The following script offers a starting point to address questions, concerns, and misinformation that frequently come up around PDA.

Sample Script

Reframe pathological demand avoidance as persistent drive for autonomy. You have read a bit about the autistic "PDA profile" and found that it resonates with your experience. Although the *DSM* does not officially recognize PDA as a diagnosis, we know quite a bit about this presentation in autistic individuals. At the same time, like many topics related to autism, the language around PDA is not ideal in a lot of ways. First, any reference to "pathological" behavior is already not very affirming of an individual's experience. Right from the start, we are referring to their experience as inherently bad and wrong. We are focusing on how the behavior impacts other people, not on what is best for the individual.

Not only that, but "demand avoidance" does not really capture the experience of many people with a PDA profile. Have you ever told your child or loved one that you need them to *not* do something, and they immediately do it? They need to feel in control of the situation, so they do the opposite of what is asked, regardless of what that is. Many in the autistic community have renamed pathological demand avoidance as persistent drive for autonomy to more accurately reflect this need for control over one's environment, life, and behaviors rather than simply a tendency to resist anything perceived as a demand. By thinking of PDA as a drive for autonomy rather than demand avoidance, we more accurately understand the individual's experience, and we recognize that there are needs underlying the behavior rather than thinking of the behaviors as problems to be solved.

Autonomy is good! Any trait or quality can be a strength or a deficit depending on the context and severity. It is not bad to want control over your life, to want to be autonomous. This is a natural part of being a human and something that we often encourage in adults.

Recognizing this fact can help you respond to PDA-based behaviors appropriately. You do not want your child or loved one to lose their drive for autonomy, though there may be moments when they need to learn skills like compromising and regulating.

Consider what kind of adult you are raising. It is tempting to correct undesired behaviors in children when we value obedience. After all, it was not that long ago that we were taught, "Children should be seen and not heard." While compliant children might fall in line and follow instructions quickly, is this really what is best for them? Children who are perfectly behaved 100 percent of the time are typically not well-adjusted; rather, they are so scared of what will happen if they step out of line. Do you want your child to obey you in all things if the cost is that they are terrified of you? Or would you prefer that your child be empowered, know how to set boundaries, and trust you with all of their emotions, even the ones that are not fun for you to see?

Additionally, consider that your child will not be a child forever. Everything you teach them now will go with them into adulthood. In the past, when parents focused on making children behave and obey, they were expected to comply with commands without question, and there was no room for them to express their own needs and preferences. As a result, they never learned skills like making micro-decisions (small choices we have to make throughout the day in order to function, even though the specific choice itself is not important). This is why many people freeze when asked what they want for dinner—they never learned how to choose because they never had the option! What kind of adult do you want your child to become? You can support your child in making their own choices and setting their own boundaries.

Your frustration is valid. You can recognize that having a drive for autonomy is valid and not want to quash this trait, while simultaneously recognizing that PDA traits can be frustrating and exhausting. It is of course inappropriate to take this frustration out on your child or loved one, but it is okay to name it. You cannot process and deal with feelings that you do not recognize. Take steps to care for yourself, get therapy and support, and do what you need to in order to self-regulate as you cope with frustrations that come up.

Safety is the top priority. While you do not want to discourage autonomy, children sometimes make unsafe choices. That is why they do not live by themselves and instead have adults to take care of them. It is your job to keep your child safe, and this is the most important thing. We will work together on communication and trust so that you can help your child understand the importance of their safety and know that there are some things you, as a parent, simply cannot compromise on.

Avoid power struggles and choose your battles. It is easy to get into spirals where everything feels like a fight, and once an argument begins, it can feel impossible to walk away. It is true that it can be harmful to set an expectation and not stand by it—this creates inconsistency, making it difficult for your child to know what you will and will not enforce. At the same time, it is essential to foster positive interactions and promote healthy attachment with your child. That means that you need to reflect on what expectations really matter and which ones you are prepared to stand by and enforce. For example, you need to stand by expectations that are necessary to keep your child safe, but you might have flexibility to let your child have a "tone" when they respond to your request.

COMMUNICATION SKILLS FOR CAREGIVERS

ALL AGES

Parents often struggle to communicate effectively with their children, and this can be even more difficult when a child experiences PDA and has unmet needs. As previously mentioned, many societal expectations for how children "should" behave and what "good" parenting looks like do not affirm the child's autonomy or help them develop into empowered adults, so even under the best of circumstances, a parent might struggle with appropriate communication. However, children with PDA traits often push back on these communication patterns more directly than children who do not have PDA traits. For this reason, it is important for therapists to work with parents on effective and healthy communication skills. The following tips are a starting point for fostering this kind of communication in the parent-child relationship.

Sample Script

It can be difficult for parents to communicate effectively with their children, and children with PDA traits are more likely to push back on the ways that adults tend to communicate with them. Here are some tips for developing effective, healthy communication with your child and supporting them in growing into an empowered adult.

Explain, but don't argue. Many autistic people struggle with following rules that they disagree with or that do not make sense to them. Because of this, it can help to clearly and concisely explain the reason why certain things are necessary. Remember, though, that you are explaining *why* something is the way that it is, not opening up a debate about whether it should stay that way. Let your child know that they can ask questions, and you will explain things to them to the best of your ability, but that you will not be changing the answer.

Be clear and precise. Many autistic people have trouble following instructions because they interpret the words in a literal sense and miss some nuance or alternative interpretation of the specific words. Sometimes this is a form of seeking autonomy—if the individual does not want to comply but feels they are not in a position to refuse, they might comply in a way that gives them a sense of control. Other times, though, autistic people honestly misunderstand what others are asking of them and get accused of defiance or resistance due to these misunderstandings. Assume good intentions, and try to be as precise as possible with your language.

Remain calm. Sometimes parents feel frustrated or even angry when their child is not doing what the parents believe the child should do. There are underlying societal issues around children's autonomy as a whole and assumptions that children must always unquestioningly obey adults, so it is not your fault if you internalized this message. At the same time, you are now responsible for doing your best for your child. While your feelings are valid, you have a responsibility to address and manage any frustration or irritation in a healthy way. In the moment, remain calm and collected, and if this is not possible, take time to collect yourself before continuing the interaction. This will also teach your child how to regulate their feelings by watching and learning from you.

Ask for clarification. As noted previously, your child will sometimes seem to act out due to an honest misunderstanding of what you expect from them. When this is the case, you can calmly and nonjudgmentally ask for clarification to better understand what is happening in the moment. If your child understands what you asked of them and they are still not complying, instead of forcing them or punishing them, get clarity on what it is about the request that they are unable to do. Does it feel too difficult for them? Are they overstimulated? Does the request interfere with their needs in some way? This can open the door to problem-solve alternatives that protect your child and get their needs met while still ensuring that necessary things are done.

Educate, but don't talk down. Many autistic people struggle to comply with rules that they do not agree with or that do not make sense to them. It can be helpful to explain the purpose of a rule or a request, but make sure that you do so in a way that invites curiosity. You are not ridiculing or talking down to your child for disagreeing; you want them to truly understand where you are coming from with the request.

Model what you want to see. Children are sponges, and they learn by watching the adults around them. Many parents notice that their child's most frustrating behaviors are a reflection of their own challenges. Make a point to engage in behavior that is the *opposite* of what frustrates you in your interactions with your child. If your child tends to yell when frustrated, consciously choose to speak at a low volume in frustrating situations. Let your child see you experiencing emotions and coping with them using healthy, appropriate skills.

"Do as I do." Take modeling a step further by working on coping skills together. Set aside time to practice regulation skills with your child. This shows them that it is okay to need this support and lets them practice when they are not escalated so that they are more likely to remember and use the skills when they need them.

Apologize when it is appropriate. No one is infallible. You will make mistakes, just like everyone else. Seeing your child as an autonomous, fully human individual deserving of respect includes acknowledging when you have made a mistake as a parent and apologizing to them. When you apologize, do not include any caveats with your apology (e.g., "I'm sorry I yelled, but when you misbehave, I get so mad"). Own what you did wrong, apologize, and make amends where appropriate. This will show your child that it is okay to make mistakes, and mistakes can be fixed. It also teaches them that they deserve respect.

THE POWER OF CHOICES

ALL AGES

Since a common trigger for difficult PDA behaviors is a need for control, we can change how we communicate expectations and give clients a sense of control over their environment by offering choices rather than making requests or giving commands. Instead of telling an individual what they need to do, find something about the task that you can give them choices about. The expectation remains that the task needs to happen, but the individual has the power to decide how it will happen. Be creative and remember that there are always choices in how something is done—your options are endless. Modeling and teaching this approach to the client's caregivers will encourage them to also support and empower their child through offering choices.

Some examples of choices you and the client's caregivers can give include:

1. Do you want to do [*task*] right now or in five minutes? (Note that you might have to come up with another choice in five minutes when it is time for the task.)

2. Do you want to do [*task 1*] first or [*task 2*] first?

3. Do you want to move quickly or slowly while you do [*task*]?

4. Do you want to play music while you do [*task*] or do it quietly?

5. Do you want to do [*task*] by yourself, or do you want me to help? (Note that you need to ensure that you are not simply doing the task for them at this point, unless that is appropriate.)

6. Which parent would you like to help you with [*task*]?

7. Which sensory item would you like with you while you do [*task*]?

TAKING BREAKS

ALL AGES

As noted in previous sections, taking breaks as needed can prevent escalation and promote the use of healthy emotion regulation skills. Unfortunately, many traditional therapies for autistic people encourage or even force the individual to remain in an overstimulating situation. Denying these breaks can lead to meltdowns, shutdowns, aggression, self-harm, and over the long term, burnout.

A neurodiversity-affirming provider encourages clients to express when they need a break and to take breaks as needed. Some caregivers express concerns that the individual will overuse this "privilege," but it builds trust when you teach an autistic person that you will support them when they express a need. In fact, an individual might request more breaks in the beginning to test whether the other person is sincere in offering this resource. Even if the individual ends up taking more breaks than they strictly "need," these added breaks can prevent further escalation. For example, someone might take extra breaks to de-escalate when they feel overwhelmed at a 3 out of 10 rather than waiting until they are at an 8.

Have a plan in place for how and where breaks can occur in session. (You might do this as part of the steps for creating a *Personalized Sensory-Friendly Space* discussed on page 58.) Have coping skills available for use during breaks so the client can de-escalate and regulate themselves. When the client indicates that they need a break, give it to them without question. If they request a break at a time when it is not possible to immediately stop a task, let them know exactly when the break can occur. For example, a child who asks to take a break in the middle of a doctor's visit might need to let the doctor finish a component of the exam before they can pause for a break. Again, this builds trust and attachment.

Encourage caregivers to take this same approach to breaks outside of session. Also remind them that sensory items used during breaks are necessities and should never be taken away as punishment. They are not toys even if they can be used for play. Think of sensory items and self-regulation breaks as needs in the same way you think of food, clothing, shelter, and bathroom access as needs. It would be abusive to tell someone that they are not permitted to eat today as punishment, and the same goes for denying a sensory break. As the individual learns to notice when they need a break, they will be better able to use skills to self-regulate in healthy and appropriate ways, and they will build trust with a caregiver who makes space for breaks.

ADDRESSING RULES

Many autistic people tend to question rules or authority rather than automatically accepting that "this is the way things are." While this quality can be a strength, many autistic people are labeled as "oppositional" or "disrespectful" for posing these questions. On a societal level, we often expect people to respect anyone labeled as an authority figure without question, but why?

Authority figures can be corrupt. Rules and laws can be unjust. If your employer instructs you to do something unethical, should you do it without question because they are your boss? When autistic people push back against authority in this way, it is often framed as a problem to be fixed because the individual is seen as noncompliant. Again, this attitude centers the impact of the individual's behavior on the people around them rather than the client's well-being. It teaches the child to comply with adults and authority figures automatically and without question to make things more convenient for the adults in charge. But teaching a child that they must obey adults without question puts the child at risk for grooming and abuse by predators who seek out children they can exploit.

This is why it is not neurodiversity-affirming or in a client's best interest to focus on teaching clients to obey rules when they have questions or concerns. Instead, when an autistic person is having trouble as a result of not following rules, have a session (or several sessions) with the caregiver and client together. In the session, have the caregiver discuss a rule that the autistic person is not following. Together, ask the client about their perception of this rule. Maybe they feel that the rule is unfair or it does not make sense to them. Maybe following the rule requires them to ignore a need. Maybe they are misunderstanding the rule.

If a rule is in place to keep the client safe, clearly and gently explain this: "We don't _____ because we could get hurt." You should also explore possible underlying unmet needs that could prevent the client from following the rule, and find safe, appropriate ways to get that need met instead. For example, a client who is using electronics without permission may be getting sensory needs met or coping with big emotions by using their device, so they take the device without permission because they are attempting to regulate and avoid a meltdown. With this in mind, how can the caregiver support the client in getting their sensory needs met? As much as possible, involve the client directly in coming up with solutions. As they build insight, they might identify appropriate solutions, and they know their own mind better than anyone else. They will also be more on board with solutions that they have a voice in choosing.

If a rule seems unfair to the client, explore this together. Why is this rule in place? Is this a neurotypical expectation that we are following because we simply never questioned it before? Being flexible and adaptable is part of being human, and caregivers can model this skill by adjusting rules in response to appropriate feedback. Essentially, your goal is to open up communication around "defiant" behavior and find solutions that empower your client, foster their autonomy, keep them safe, and stimulate healthy communication with caregivers.

MANAGING EXPECTATIONS

ALL AGES

This intervention focuses on caregiver expectations for their autistic loved one. Parents especially often have expectations before having children. They have a vision for their child's life and future, and often an autism diagnosis subverts these expectations. This is the subject of "Welcome to Holland" by Emily Perl Kingsley, which describes the experience of raising a child with a disability using the analogy of someone who planned to travel to Italy but ended up in Holland instead. The essay recognizes the disappointment and struggles that come with ending up somewhere other than you expected, where you do not speak the language and where your guidebooks cannot help you, while also recognizing that Holland can be just as fantastic as Italy.

While this piece can be a good starting point in getting parents to acknowledge and work through their emotions around their child's diagnosis, it is reflective of a deeper societal problem: People enter parenthood with predetermined expectations, which sets the child up for failure. This is not specific to autism—for example, a parent who expects their child to be heterosexual and cisgender may express disappointment that their child is LGBTQ+, or a parent who wants their child to have a certain career may pressure them to pursue majors and jobs that are not the child's dream.

Parenthood is about supporting a child in their life journey, not about raising a specific type of child. When a parent comes in with expectations for their child, whether those expectations are about the child's appearance, abilities, strengths, gender, neurotype, or any other piece of that child's identity, the child picks up on this, even if they are not consciously aware of it. The most supportive parent in the world who enters parenthood with these expectations risks sending the message that their child is inadequate or insufficient for being their authentic self. This decimates the child's self-esteem and can cause masking, as children want to be accepted and loved, and a child who realizes that their authentic self does not match their parent's expectations might try to change themselves to fit in with what they think their parent wants from them.

It might not be the parent's fault that they entered parenthood with predetermined expectations for who their child would become, but it is their responsibility to confront and address this bias so they do not harm their child. It is often beneficial for parents to get their own therapy to address their emotions around their child's diagnosis and to work through this so they can authentically show up and support their child. As a clinician, you should have a set of referrals to provide resources and support for caregivers who need to work through their expectations for their child.

WHAT CAN YOU CONTROL?

Unfortunately, no matter who you are or what you are doing, there will always be certain factors in life that are outside of your control. It can be challenging and frustrating to have to do things you do not want to do or that do not make sense to you. To help your client counter this frustration, work together to make a list of things that *are* within their control. Note that many autistic people are not in control of their bodies during meltdowns, so sometimes prepopulated lists can be invalidating and nonaffirming if they indicate that you can control your body or your emotional response to a situation. Because each person has a different level of control over their environment, their body, and certain situations, creating an open-ended list can prevent accidental invalidation.

If the client is struggling to come up with things that are in their control, you might suggest the following examples, while remembering to consider whether each example is actually true for that specific client:

1. I can control my decision to ask to take a break.

2. I can control choosing to do one of my stims.

3. I can control whether I focus on an affirming thought.

4. I can control my choice to ask for help.

5. I can control how deep my breath is.

AUTONOMY: IT'S YOUR CHOICE

ALL AGES

While there may be times when you need to redirect behavior for safety reasons, it is vital that you do not undermine anyone's autonomy. When autistic children, especially those with PDA traits, are taught that compliance is more important than their comfort and well-being, they are at increased risk for mistreatment and abuse. They learn that they should put authority ahead of their own needs, a quality predators look for.

To emphasize the importance of autonomy, work with your client and their caregiver to explain the concept. For young kids or those with limited comprehension of verbal language, you can explain autonomy this way:

> Every single human has the right to feel safe and comfortable. This means that we all have the right to be in charge of certain things with our bodies. For example, you have the right to move in ways that help you when you are having difficult feelings, so it is not okay for me to take away a stim toy that you are using. Since everyone has this right, it also means that I have the right for other people to not hurt me, so it would not be okay for you to hit me. The right to be in charge of what happens to our bodies is called *autonomy*.

Of course, autonomy is not about doing everything you want all the time. There is more nuance to the topic. You can explain this to your client this way:

> Although you have the right to be in charge of your body, there are some things your caregiver needs you to do. There are times when they need you to listen for your safety or to make sure that they are doing their job to take care of you. That means that, even though you have autonomy, your caregiver might stop you if you are trying to hurt yourself, or they might encourage you to try foods that have nutrients you need. We need to work together to make sure your caregiver is giving you autonomy and also making sure that you understand and listen when they are doing their job to take care of you and keep you safe.

Address any questions the client or their caregiver has about this. Have the caregiver provide examples of situations where the client struggled with listening, and have them come up with examples of times when they did not respect the client's right to autonomy. Honoring both sides communicates to the client that their caregiver is prioritizing their well-being and making an effort to ensure their autonomy is respected in the future. Otherwise, the client might see requests to change behavior as an infringement on their autonomy. Differentiating these concepts in this way ensures that the client continues to understand their rights and helps keep them safe.

SUPER DEMAND AVOIDANCE

AGES 8+

PDA traits can present challenges for people in the autistic person's life, but there are ways in which these traits can also be a strength. This activity aims to both validate these difficulties *and* take a strengths-based approach in understanding PDA. Although it is important to depathologize these traits and promote autonomy, be mindful of falling into the trap of toxic positivity. You must not invalidate a client's experiences when they feel frustrated by PDA traits or tell a client that they are not experiencing a disability when they actually are. You are merely pointing out that the client also has strengths, and they are not inherently bad as a result of who they are. Because this reframe requires buy-in and a shift in attitude from caretakers, this intervention works best with the family together. The following is a script you can use to guide this conversation.

Sample Script

We know that sometimes you have a hard time doing things that [*caregiver*] asks of you. We know that, for many autistic people, being told they *have* to do something can cause them to become defensive because they have a strong need to feel in control of themselves and their life. Sometimes, this causes problems because other people assume the autistic person is being "difficult" on purpose, when they are really trying to get a need met. It can be very frustrating to feel misunderstood and to feel like other people are telling you what to do! On the other hand, being able to stand up for yourself is a good quality. It is okay and good to stand up to bullies and injustice. If someone is mistreating you, [*caregiver*] wants you to speak up and defend yourself.

So, you can think of your need for autonomy as a superpower. Think about how every superhero has powers that make them really strong and powerful, but also vulnerabilities that can cause them problems. Sometimes, your superpower keeps you safe by reminding you that you have the right to stand up for yourself. Other times, it causes problems, like if [*caregiver*] is asking you to do something for your health or safety but you don't want to do it. Let's use the *I Am a Superhero!* worksheet to explore how you have both powers and vulnerabilities as a result of your brain's strong need for autonomy.

I Am a Superhero!

My Powers	My Vulnerabilities
1. _____	1. _____
2. _____	2. _____
3. _____	3. _____
4. _____	4. _____

BEHAVIOR AS COMMUNICATION: WHAT DO YOU NEED?

ALL AGES

This intervention is for caregivers and aims to shift how they respond to PDA behaviors that they frame as "bad" or "problematic." Many parenting philosophies focus on punishing undesirable behaviors to create compliance, but that does not mean it is a healthy or safe practice. A child who is too terrified of their parent to express an emotion or act out in any way is not a well-adjusted child.

In addition, given the nature of PDA, punishment is counterproductive. It results in a cycle that goes like this: The autistic client refuses a request or command, the caretaker punishes them, the autistic person digs their heels in, the parent punishes them more, and the autistic person digs in more, until the attachment bond is destroyed. In some cases, the autistic person "gives in" and begins masking, stops trusting the caregiver, and is put on the path for burnout. Neither outcome is in the client's best interest.

Therefore, after providing caregivers with background information about what PDA is, how it manifests, and why the end goal of compliance is inappropriate, you can work with them to begin to change how they view these behaviors. As always, tweak the script that follows based on what is accurate and appropriate for a given client and their family.

Sample Script

I know that [*client's*] behavior is sometimes frustrating, and there are times when you need to redirect them for safety or other reasons. It is valid that you feel angry about these behaviors, but channeling that anger into punishment is not helpful or effective. Because of how [*client's*] brain works, punishment will only cause them to dig in harder and further resist what you want them to do. It also causes their brain to associate you with punishment rather than safety and security.

If you are thinking that you *never* would have behaved that way around your parents, this might be true, but I want you to think about something. Try to remember a time when you had a really big emotion in childhood, when you might have felt the way that [*client*] feels when they are [*specific PDA behavior*]. Even though you felt that way, you wouldn't have let your parents see that side of you. Why is that? Is there something your parents would have done to you that your child believes you would never do to them?

You are not raising a compliant child. You are raising a future adult. Do you want them to be able to stand up for themselves when something is wrong? Do you want them to be able to get their needs met? Or do you want them to unquestioningly go along with anything an authority figure asks of them?

Behaviors are a form of communication. Everything [*client*] does communicates what they need in that moment. I want you to try to let go of the idea that they need to be punished when they have a behavior that you don't want them to have. Instead, assume that [*client*] wants a healthy attachment to you, that they want to make good choices and rise to your expectations.

It might not always feel that way. We all say and do unacceptable things sometimes, especially when we have a big, unpleasant emotion. It can be easy to fall into patterns of behavior too—if someone gets into trouble frequently, they might assume that they will be in trouble no matter what they do, so they might feel angry with their caretaker and act out more often. But all behavior is a form of communication. [*Client*] needs a connection to you. They need your attention and focus. When they feel like they only get that connection when they act out, they are going to act out more often in order to get that connection the only way they know how. [*Use other specific behavior examples, and prompt the caregiver to try to think of what need might be underneath each.*]

Now, when you think of behavior as an effort to get a need met rather than as deliberate defiance, how do you respond? I want you to use the *Behavior Tracking Log* to track some behaviors you see in [*client*] and note how these behaviors might communicate needs.

Behavior Tracking Log

Date and Time	Situation	Behavior	Possible Need Communicated

Communication Interventions

Autism is marked by social and communication difficulties, and while some of these difficulties come from societal standards and neurotypical definitions of "appropriate" communication, many autistic people struggle to express themselves in a way that the people around them can understand. It is not our place to tell an individual what their experience with communication difficulties is, or to debate whether these difficulties are due to systems issues or a disability. However, we can help support autistic clients and their caregivers in developing forms of communication that allow the autistic person to express themselves in a way that is comfortable for them and that their caretaker can understand.

Many traditional therapies for autistic people address communication difficulties by attempting to force the autistic person to use "mouth words" to fit in with mainstream communication methods. While some autistic people might find these interventions helpful, you must remember that it is harmful to prioritize one method of communication over others simply because it is convenient for others in the client's life. There are many ways to communicate effectively, and none are inherently superior to others.

While the terms *communication skills* and *social skills* are sometimes used interchangeably, it is important to know that these terms do not mean the same thing. Social skills are those used to interact and foster relationships with other people. The concept of social skills in the field favors the ways that neurotypical people tend to interact with and understand each other, and many autistic people are subject to "social skills training" as another way of teaching them forced masking and sending the message that their preferred interaction styles are inherently wrong. Communication skills, on the other hand, are methods to help individuals express needs in a way that the people around them can clearly understand and then offer adequate support. The goal of the interventions in this chapter is to help autistic people express themselves and be understood, not to teach them that their interaction styles are wrong and require correction.

When developing communication interventions, particularly those for semispeaking or nonspeaking clients, make sure that you listen to and elevate the experiences of members of this community. This book includes examples that I gathered from a variety of sources, but since I am not a member of the semispeaking or nonspeaking communities, my expertise should not overshadow the communities represented.

Language note: According to the Autistic Self Advocacy Network, *nonspeaking* is the preferred term for an autistic person who never uses mouth words to communicate. Some in the autistic community have expressed that the term *nonverbal* implies that the individual cannot comprehend verbal language, and many nonspeaking autistics can comprehend receptive verbal language, so this is not accurate.

In addition, some autistic people are able to communicate using mouth words some of the time but lose this ability during burnout, during periods of stress, or at seemingly unpredictable times. For these individuals, use of the term *nonspeaking* is misleading and can lead to reduced supports for autistic people who can never communicate this way, as it reinforces the idea that a nonspeaking person could speak with mouth words "if they really wanted to." Although I was unable to find surveys of the autistic community showing majority preference, many nonspeaking autistic advocates have described these episodes as "losing speech" rather than "becoming nonverbal" for clarity.

All alternative forms of communication described in this section can benefit nonspeaking autistic people as well as those who lose speech in certain situations or at certain times. As always, honor the language preferences of individual clients within the context of their treatment and in their sessions.

AUGMENTATIVE AND ALTERNATIVE COMMUNICATION

AGES 2+

Augmentative and alternative communication (AAC) describes the range of devices that allow an individual to either type words or select images to communicate without having to speak verbally. The device then reads the words out loud. Technically, a pen and pad of paper are a type of AAC, but more advanced devices exist. There are also AAC apps that can be downloaded onto a smartphone or tablet. Some highly rated apps include:

- **Proloquo2Go AAC:** At the time of writing, this app has a 4.8 rating from more than 8,500 users. It costs $249.99 to download and has additional in-app purchases. The user taps images or words to express themselves, and it is fully customizable according to the developers. It comes preloaded with words and phrases that research shows are most commonly used, with the option to create your own. The app contains images of people with customizable skin tone as well. Users can choose what voice reads their message, including different genders, ages, and accents.

- **Visuals2Go:** This app was created for children and educators. It has a 4.3 rating from more than 1,300 users and is free to download, though you must make in-app upgrades to access all features. It uses preset images and cards to help communicate needs and basic concepts.

- **Predictable:** This app has a 4.5 rating from more than 100 users and costs $159.99 to download. It does not indicate that users will be subject to additional in-app purchases. Users can type out words, use word prediction to communicate faster, or choose from images. They can save common phrases for single-press communication. It also has head and face tracking that can allow clients to use the app through facial expressions and gestures. There are multiple voices to choose from and the option to tweak the rate and pitch of a preloaded voice for further customization.

- **Spoken—Tap to Talk AAC:** This app has more than 100 user reviews and a 4.4 rating. It uses text and is designed for teens and adults who are able to read. It uses real voices for more natural speech. It is free to download but requires in-app purchases to access all features.

- **Speech Assistant AAC:** Although this app only has 50 user ratings, it has a score of 4.8. It is $22.99 to download and does not have additional purchases in the app. Users can make phone and video calls, allowing them to communicate over the phone straight from the app. It has fully customizable text and image-based communication.

When choosing a device or app, consider what symbols or preloaded words would be most helpful (i.e., things the client needs to communicate often or quickly); whether the client prefers images, pregenerated words, or typing; whether they want the app to read their messages out loud; and the customization options. The client or their caregiver can then download the app that best meets their needs onto their device. I recommend creating a shortcut for the app so the client can find it quickly and easily whenever they need to.

While most AAC apps indicate that they are designed for ages four and up, the American Speech-Language-Hearing Association reports that children under age three can successfully use AAC.

SPELLING

While AAC devices and apps can allow for nonspeaking autistic people to spell out what they are trying to communicate, if a device is not available, you can keep a letter board available for clients to spell out what they want to say. Due to fine motor issues, clients may benefit from a plastic letter board with letters cut out, which allows them to clearly indicate which letters they are selecting using a pencil. For those able to point with their finger, a printed alphabet on laminated paper can also allow them to communicate through spelling. If you regularly work with nonspeaking clients, have these options available at all times so that the client is always able to communicate directly.

A B C D E F G H I J K L M N
O P Q R S T U V W X Y Z
0 1 2 3 4 5 6 7 8 9
! ? # & $ % ^ @ * ( )
− + = [ ] { } : ; ' " . , < >

SIGN LANGUAGE

ALL AGES

Sign language is a language of hand gestures and signs that communicate words and ideas. There are many different types of sign language, just like there are many different verbal languages around the world. Many in the Deaf community use sign language as a primary means of communication, though hearing people who do not use mouth words for various reasons can communicate through sign language too.

A nonspeaking autistic person who is comfortable communicating through sign language should have the opportunity to learn sign language rather than being forced to use mouth words. If the autistic person is also deaf, caregivers should also learn sign language to communicate back to their loved one. However, if the autistic person is hearing and comfortable with spoken language from the people around them, the caregiver can learn to understand sign language but speak verbally in response.

INFO CARDS

Info cards are preprinted visual tools that nonspeaking individuals or those who lose speech can use to communicate their needs quickly and easily. Clients who are overwhelmed by the choices in an AAC device might benefit from info cards to allow them to still express certain phrases.

For efficiency, info cards should clearly indicate what the person is trying to say using both words and an image to allow the client to quickly find what they are looking for. Typically, an individual will only carry a few info cards so that they do not become overwhelmed or lose track of which card they are looking for.

There are many info cards available for purchase or free download, or you can work with your client to make their own set based on the specific things they want to make sure they can communicate at any given time. Options for info cards can include:

- Yes/no to answer basic questions.
- I need food/water/to use the bathroom.
- I am overstimulated.
- I need help. (This card can also help when the client is out by themselves and does not have the caregiver around.)
- I am [*diagnosis or identity term*] and am unable to communicate with words. (Again, this is helpful for clients who are in spaces where the people around them do not know their needs.)

BODY LANGUAGE AND GESTURES

AGES 4+

Some autistic people struggle with using words, even in writing or through an AAC device. In particular, those who have selective mutism might be unable to provide written responses when activated or anxious. If your client struggles with this, work with them and their caregiver together to identify specific body language signs that indicate the client needs support. The caregiver should look for these cues to support the client and get them out of situations where they are uncomfortable or beginning to escalate and are unable to express this clearly. Additionally, having a specific gesture in place allows the client to express a specific, simple concept like "I need to take a break" or "I need to leave this place," without having to pull the caregiver aside and explain it to them.

This kind of signal or cue only works if the caregiver understands the importance of listening and honoring the client's expressed need. If the client uses the agreed-upon gesture but the caregiver does not respond appropriately and help them, they are unlikely to try again. This is why education is so important.

Have the client choose a gesture or indicator that they will be able to perform even when they are struggling, and practice in the session how the caregiver will respond when it is used. The gesture can include a particular wave, signaling with a finger, or any sign that the client feels they would be able to use as needed and that the caregiver will recognize.

CODES AND KEYWORDS

AGES 4+

Some clients are able to use mouth words some or all of the time and might be able to use a specific key phrase or code word to express their needs in the moment. Having a code word to indicate the need for support or a break is a good start, and you can choose code words that have different meanings. For example, some caregivers express sadness that their autistic loved one does not express affection in the same way as nonautistic people tend to (e.g., hugs or other forms of touch). They might pressure their loved one to express affection in neurotypical ways, either intentionally or unintentionally, which places additional stress on the autistic person. Because this reinforces the idea that the autistic person's natural communication preferences are insufficient or less than, it can help to determine code words so that the guardian understands that their loved one is expressing affection. Possible code phrases include:

- I love you.

- Thank you.

- I'm glad you are here. (Or even just "I'm glad.")

Although codes can include words, if the autistic person enjoys making different kinds of sounds, this can be incorporated as well. For example, some autistic people enjoy making animal noises and might decide that a meow means "I love you!" It's important that the client and their caretaker come together to make sure that both understand what different words and sounds will mean and how the caregiver will respond when the client indicates these cues.

SELF-EXPRESSION: BLACKOUT POETRY

AGES 8+

This activity is for clients who can read and express themselves in writing. Sometimes it can be difficult to find words to express what we are feeling, and creative expression can bridge the gap. Blackout poetry involves taking a page that already has words written on it and blacking out certain words so the remaining words create a poem. For example, you could tear a page out of this book and cross out words to make it say something completely different. You can use old books set for recycling, printed pages of literature that resonate with your client, or print media like newspapers or magazines.

For clients who prefer to work digitally, you can paste text into a document and have them use the highlighter feature to black out words they want to cover up. An added benefit of this tool is that they can undo any words they did not intend to cover. There are also a couple of websites that allow you to create blackout poetry online:

- https://blackout-poetry-generator.vercel.app
- https://blackoutpoetry.glitch.me

This is a simple and easy tool to get clients communicating when they are struggling to come up with words on their own.

USING PRECISE LANGUAGE

ALL AGES

Because autistic people sometimes process things in a concrete and literal manner, miscommunications often arise with caregivers who process language differently. This can occur when a nonautistic caregiver misunderstands the autistic person's intent or when an autistic caregiver does not process things in the same way as the client. Remember, all autistic people are individuals and can process things differently.

Encourage caregivers to be as precise as possible in the language they use and seek clarification. Every communication can be broken down into three parts:

1. What was said

2. What was meant

3. What was heard

Miscommunication happens when these three parts do not coincide with each other. Consider the following example: A child is playing a video game, and their parent tells them to turn off the game and come to the table for dinner. The child says okay and continues playing the game. The parent is angry that the child did not comply, and the child is confused about why they are in trouble. Broken down, here is what happened:

- The parent said, "Turn off your game and come to the table, please."

- The parent meant, "Follow my command right now."

- The client heard, "Turn off your game when you get to a break."

- The client said, "Okay."

- The client meant, "I will do what you said in a minute."

- The parent heard, "I will come right now," and then the child did not follow through.

Both parties think they were clear in their intent and believe they listened to the other person, but since the parent was not precise enough in their language, there was a gap in communication.

Consider another example: One partner asks the other, "Do you think you can wash the dishes?" The other partner says, "Yes." That partner does not wash the dishes. The first partner is frustrated, and the second partner is confused. Here is what happened:

- The first partner said, "Do you think you can wash the dishes?"

- They meant, "Please wash the dishes."

- The second partner heard, "Are you physically able to wash the dishes?"

- They answered that yes, they are physically able to wash dishes.

- The first partner thinks the second partner chose not to do something they agreed to do.

- The second partner thinks they simply answered a direct question.

In moments of miscommunication, have caregivers gently, calmly, and nonjudgmentally request clarification. Help them to identify where communication broke down and offer more specific language in the future.

Trauma Interventions

As I have discussed at length, autistic individuals are more likely than nonautistic individuals to experience abuse and other traumatic events in childhood. This is not to mention that existing as an autistic person in this world, which is not designed to meet their needs, is stressful and can cause ongoing trauma. In recognizing this, neurodiversity-affirming providers must also be trauma-informed in their work.

Although you can be trauma-informed with any intervention, the activities listed in this section have the specific goal of helping clients work through trauma symptoms. They are intended as accessible, ready-to-implement tools that you can generally use with clients across a variety of ages. As you go through these interventions, keep in mind that trauma work can be exhausting. Remember to regularly check in with your client and save time at the end of each appointment to process, de-escalate, and work through any residual feelings elicited by the interventions. You can additionally prepare clients and their caregivers for possible emotions that may arise after trauma sessions. As always, it is inappropriate to pressure or force a client to address trauma before they are ready or if they indicate discomfort with a specific intervention.

TIMELINE ACTIVITY

This activity taps into a narrative approach to processing trauma. To begin, ask your client how they feel about creating a timeline of their life. Let them know that this can help you process things from their past together, and it gives you helpful information about what they have been through. If they consent to the activity, work with them to decide how they want to put the project together: Do they want to write a narrative story using words or poetry, or do they want to create a visual art piece, such as a drawing or a collage? Whichever communication style fits best for the client is most appropriate.

Next, determine how you want to break up the client's past. Do they want to focus on each year individually or a chunk of time (like two to five years)? Larger portions of time can be helpful for clients who struggle with remote memory, as they do not have to recall specifically when each event occurred and can instead share more generally about larger periods.

You can be nondirective and open with this activity if you choose, letting the client include whatever they want and leaving out anything they deem irrelevant or are not ready to dig into. On the other hand, if the client prefers or needs more direction, you can use the following prompts for each time period on the timeline, remembering that clients can choose to skip prompts that do not apply to them or that they find triggering:

1. How old were you during this time?
2. Where did you live, and with whom?
3. What was going well at this time?
4. What were some of your favorite things at this time?
5. What is your favorite memory from this time?
6. Who were the important people in your life?
7. What was not going well at that time?
8. What things were happening then that you are glad are not happening anymore?
9. What things were happening then that you miss now?

When your client has crafted a timeline of their past, include a section on the present. Again, you can take a nondirective approach in asking the client to describe their life as it is now, or you can use these questions as a starting point:

1. How old are you?

2. Where do you live and with whom?

3. What is going well?

4. What are your favorite things?

5. What things are you good at?

6. Who are the important people in your life?

7. Who are your friends?

8. What things are not going well?

9. What things do you wish would stop?

Finally, have the client craft a future section. They can choose to break this section down to indicate where they think or hope they will be in 5, 10, 15, and 20 years, or they can simply have one section focused on their future. Possible prompts to explore include:

1. Where do you hope you will live?

2. What do you hope you will be doing?

3. What things do you hope you will be good at?

4. What things do you think might be difficult for you?

5. What things are you worried might happen?

6. What things do you hope will happen?

Before engaging in this activity, it is important that clients have adequate coping skills to manage and address the variety of feelings that may come up as they rehash their trauma memories. Exploring these historical events can retrigger trauma and stress, evoke feelings of grief over things the client has lost, or result in feelings of anger at things they have dealt with in the past. Clients need to understand the risks associated with the activity before proceeding to ensure that they understand what they are agreeing to, and they need appropriate skills in place to manage these emotions if and when they come up.

MY LEFT-HANDED BRAIN

AGES 5+

This educational intervention helps autistic clients understand how their brains work differently than nonautistic brains, reframing "deficits" as neutral differences. Remember that deficits and disabilities are not immoral or a negative reflection of an individual's character, so it is okay if a client has and is aware of deficits. At the same time, normalizing the existence of different neurotypes from a neutral standpoint can address the trauma and self-esteem deficits that come from living in a world not designed for how their brain works. The following script uses a neutral analogy of right-handedness versus left-handedness to illustrate the brain differences between autistic and nonautistic individuals.

Sample Script

Not that long ago, a lot of people believed there was only one way to write correctly: with your right hand. People who used their left hand were punished and forced to use their right hand even though that didn't come naturally to them. Do you know anyone who is left-handed? Is the way they write bad or wrong? Of course not!

Now, we let people write with whichever hand is comfortable, and we don't tell left-handed people that they have to change or use the hand that isn't comfortable for them. Even though we changed how we think about being left-handed, we still design a lot of things with the assumption that everyone can comfortably use their right hand, like gearshifts on cars and doorknobs. As a result, left-handed people still have shorter life expectancy than right-handed people—they get into more accidents simply because we don't bother to make things designed for their dominant hand, or we only provide those things when they specifically ask for them or pay extra.

Being autistic is kind of like having a left-handed brain. Some people think you should force your brain to be right-handed even though that is not possible, and trying to pretend otherwise can cause a lot of harm. Even when the people who support you make space for you to use your brain the way that comes naturally to you, the world is designed for people with right-handed brains. That is why some things feel so difficult. Even though your brain isn't less or worse because you are autistic, you still face challenges because we don't have systems in place that cater to "left-handed" brains the way we do for "right-handed" brains.

IDENTIFYING YOUR TRIGGERS

AGES 5+

Many of the activities in the interoception section of this book teach clients how to be more aware of what is going on in their bodies and how they emotionally respond to the world around them. For those with a trauma history, this improved insight can help them start to recognize triggers for trauma or overstimulation. As clients develop this skill, they can use the following *Trigger Log* to keep track of instances when they are starting to struggle with big emotions and behaviors. Caregivers can help track these events if the client is unable to document them independently but should take care to ensure that the client is aware that they are not in trouble when the caregiver documents it for them.

If the client has trouble identifying a specific event that led them to exhibit big emotions or behaviors, that is okay! Sometimes feelings get big quickly, and clients might not recognize them until they are ready to burst. Additionally, as discussed in previous sections, individuals who mask often purposely detach from their emotional needs as a protective mechanism. If your client has difficulties coming up with any triggers, you can explore this in session and see if you can find any patterns or precipitating events together. Note that not every situation will have an identifiable trigger, though this intervention can be a starting point for reducing distress and helping clients manage any triggers that are avoidable.

Trigger Log

Date and Time	What Was the Triggering Event?	What Emotions Did You Feel?	How Did You Behave in Response?

MOOD TRACKING

AGES 6+

A mood tracker is a tool to help clients notice their emotions in real time and uncover possible triggers for different moods. It differs from the previous *Identifying Your Triggers* activity in that clients are prompted to note their mood whether or not they have experienced a precipitating event. Because mood tracking asks clients to observe their moods on a regular basis, as opposed to in response to a triggering stimulus, it can be appropriate for clients who become anxious or distressed when they are asked to think about triggers. However, they can be overwhelming for some, so choose your interventions based on the individual client's needs.

Clients can choose whether they want to track their overall mood for the day or break the day down into parts. Some might find the single-day optional more manageable, though this approach might reinforce the idea that a negative event "spoils" the entire day, so they may benefit from noting changes in mood throughout the day. Collaborate with your client to figure out what type of tracker is best for them. The following pages contain two different options you can choose from.

Have your client choose how many different moods they want to track, and if they struggle with this, you can always start with a few basic options, like happy, sad, angry, and scared. You can assign a color to each mood and invite the client to use markers or colored pencils to indicate which mood they felt each day or at particular times of the day. (If the client does not like color coding their moods, they can always just write the mood in each space.) Review patterns together and note what circumstances and events put the client in pleasant or unpleasant moods.

Weekly Mood Tracker Option 1

	Monday	Tuesday	Wednesday	Thursday	Friday	Saturday	Sunday
Overall Mood							
Overall Mood							
Overall Mood							
Overall Mood							

Color Key:

☐	Happy	☐	Scared
☐	Sad	☐	Angry

Notes: _____
_____
_____

Weekly Mood Tracker Option 2

	Monday	Tuesday	Wednesday	Thursday	Friday	Saturday	Sunday
Wake up							
Morning							
Early afternoon							
Mid afternoon							
Evening							
Bedtime							

Color Key:

☐	Happy	☐	Scared
☐	Sad	☐	Angry

Notes:

_____

_____

_____

_____

THOUGHT STOPPING: DON'T THINK ABOUT A BLUE SQUIRREL

AGES 5+

When we experience distressing or intrusive thoughts, we are tempted to push them down and ignore them, but that is ineffective, as focusing our attention on getting rid of the thought is the same thing as focusing on the thought itself. Since clients often get down on themselves for focusing on thoughts they would rather get rid of, this educational activity helps them understand why this pattern occurs and teaches them how to respond in a more helpful way.

Remember that everyone's brain processes differently. Many therapeutic scripts assume that people think a certain way, such as having a constant internal monologue or thinking in words. However, people's cognitive experiences differ—some people do not think in words at all, and some people go for periods without thoughts. The sample script is written with this in mind.

Sample Script

Thoughts can come up at any time, even if you don't intend for them to. You might have thoughts about something you did in the past, something you are looking forward to, or something completely random. Thoughts can pop into your head as phrases, images, or something else—and you don't have any control over it. This is all normal!

Sometimes the thoughts that you experience might be scary, unpleasant, or just unhelpful. You might not like those thoughts and wish that they would go away. This is easier said than done because, like I said, you don't control all of your thoughts.

Let's try an experiment. Whatever you do, no matter what, for the next 10 seconds, do not think about a blue squirrel. Don't think the words *blue* or *squirrel*, don't picture a blue squirrel in your brain, and don't have any thoughts related to blue squirrels. Ready? I'll keep time.

[*After 10 seconds*] What were you thinking about? I bet that whatever you tried to focus your thoughts on, blue squirrels popped up in there somewhere. That's because you can't just tell yourself *not* to think about something. In fact, telling yourself to ignore a thought can make the thought louder or more prominent in your brain.

It's the same thing that happens when you have scary thoughts about a bad thing that happened to you. It's really hard to make those thoughts go away, which is why you want to *replace* them with another thought instead. Let's choose something you want to decide to think about instead when these thoughts come up. What kind of thought would be helpful to you in that moment? It's most helpful if you choose something that makes you feel calm and relaxed. Don't be afraid to get creative when thinking of ideas! You can use an affirmation, an image, a memory, a stim, a song, or any other type of thought to focus your attention on. This could be a phrase like "I am doing my best," a thought about a person you care about and trust, or your favorite song—any of these can help you redirect your thoughts.

SELF-CARE CHECKLIST

AGES 6+

Because autistic people often experience sensory issues, certain self-care tasks can be challenging for them, such as brushing their hair or teeth, bathing, or dressing appropriately for the weather. In addition, many individuals have trauma as a result of being forced to do these tasks despite the discomfort or even pain it caused. When someone has a sensory issue around a self-care task, they are often invalidated and told that they are wrong about their own experience.

For example, as discussed earlier, many autistic people have limited food preferences. In childhood, they might have told a parent or guardian that they did not feel comfortable eating something—only to be told, "You have to eat it," without the caregiver trying to find a solution that works for the child or that helps them feel comfortable. This teaches the child that (1) the person in charge of taking care of them will not keep them safe from uncomfortable experiences, (2) their perception of reality is wrong, and (3) they have to do things that are uncomfortable for them because their discomfort does not matter. For some, the discomfort becomes more intense over time because they were not permitted to address it and self-regulate, which can lead to meltdowns when presented with the task or an inability to attempt the task at all. It is important to validate and honor an autistic person's experience regardless of the task.

At the same time, some self-care tasks need to happen. For example, hair brushing can be overstimulating to many autistic people, but if they fully neglect their hair for too long, it can become painfully matted. Rather than saying, "It hurts you to have your hair brushed, so we will not brush your hair at all," focus on finding a way to provide hair care that is comfortable for the client. This might mean adopting a low-maintenance hairstyle, finding a brush with a different texture, or keeping the hair in braids so that it does not get as tangled.

The following set of self-care checklists help clients identify what tasks *need* to happen for their well-being and help them identify safe and comfortable ways to meet these self-care needs. The gentle approach allows the client to get around their trauma history associated with these tasks. Maintain open communication, and validate the client's concerns and worries as they come up.

Self-Care Checklist: Caring for Your Body

What things do you need to do to care for your body? To take care of your health and physical well-being?

1. _____

2. _____

3. _____

4. _____

5. _____

What do you experience when trying to do each of these things? This can include body sensations, emotions, memories, and so forth.

1. _____

2. _____

3. _____

4. _____

5. _____

Problem-solve: How can you change each task so that it meets your sensory needs?

1. _____

2. _____

3. _____

4. _____

5. _____

Self-Care Checklist: Caring for Your Mind

What things do you need to do to care for your emotional state? To take care of your mental health and well-being?

1. _____

2. _____

3. _____

4. _____

5. _____

What do you experience when trying to do each of these things? This can include body sensations, emotions, memories, and so forth.

1. _____

2. _____

3. _____

4. _____

5. _____

Problem-solve: How can you change each task so that it meets your sensory needs?

1. _____

2. _____

3. _____

4. _____

5. _____

Self-Care Checklist: Caring for Your Living Space

What things do you need to do to care for your home or room? To make sure it is a safe and nurturing place for you to live?

1. _____

2. _____

3. _____

4. _____

5. _____

What do you experience when trying to do each of these things? This can include body sensations, emotions, memories, and so forth.

1. _____

2. _____

3. _____

4. _____

5. _____

Problem-solve: How can you change each task so that it meets your sensory needs?

1. _____

2. _____

3. _____

4. _____

5. _____

YOUR STIMULATION LEVEL

Autistic meltdowns occur when an individual is so overstimulated that they can no longer self-regulate. There is often buildup to a meltdown, but when caregivers, authority figures, and other adults invalidate the individual and force them to remain in settings that are harming them, this leads to more frequent meltdowns. Often, the autistic person is then blamed for the outburst and told that they are causing problems and being difficult on purpose.

An important part of addressing this trauma is helping the autistic person get back in touch with their stimulation level and receive adequate support in bringing it down. This may include stepping away and taking a break or using coping items in their sensory space. It is important to remember that each client will have different needs and skills that bring down their big emotions. Not only will this teach them to get back in touch with and communicate their needs, but it will show them that these needs are valid, and their caregiver will support them in getting their needs met.

Use the *Your Stimulation Level* worksheet that follows to help your client identify the body signals that reflect their stimulation level in a given moment. The levels presented indicate when the individual is doing fine (level 0), when they are starting to have trouble (level 1), when they need something urgently (level 2), when they are on the verge of a meltdown (level 3), and when they are already melting down (level 4). If a client is not used to checking in with their body cues, they might not be able to identify their stimulation level until it is very intense at first. However, over time, they should be able to identify less intense body cues as they arise, especially if the caregiver teaches them that their needs will be honored.

Your Stimulation Level

Level 0: I feel fine. I am comfortable and calm in my environment.

Here are the body cues that let me know I am at level 0:

1. _____
2. _____
3. _____
4. _____
5. _____

Level 1: I am feeling slightly stimulated. I am aware of some things in my environment that are not comfortable for me, but I am able to tolerate them.

Here are the body cues that let me know I am at level 1:

1. _____
2. _____
3. _____
4. _____
5. _____

Level 2: I am starting to feel overstimulated. I can continue to tolerate my environment but will need to leave or receive support soon, within the next 10 minutes.

Here are the body cues that let me know I am at level 2:

1. _____
2. _____
3. _____
4. _____
5. _____

Level 3: I am overstimulated. I need immediate support because I cannot tolerate my current environment.

Here are the body cues that let me know I am at level 3:

1. _____

2. _____

3. _____

4. _____

5. _____

Level 4: I am having a meltdown.

Here are the body cues that let me know I am at level 4:

1. _____

2. _____

3. _____

4. _____

5. _____

FLASHBACK STOPPING

AGES 8+

When trauma flashbacks occur, they can feel very real, and it can seem impossible to get them to stop. A client who experiences these flashbacks can feel like they are literally reliving the traumatic experience and may have trouble pulling themselves out of the memory. For autistic clients in particular, flashbacks can interfere with communication skills—an autistic person might shut down or lose speech during a flashback and not be able to indicate what is going on or ask for help. This is why it is important to practice skills ahead of time and have strategies set up for caregivers to offer support.

To bring themselves back to the present moment, your client can use the following script, which prompts them to orient themselves to their current surroundings. The client should go through the script (out loud or in their mind) and process each step on their own or with the help of a caregiver if they struggle to use coping skills during flashbacks.

Clients who process information verbally can use the written script. Those who are nonspeaking or semispeaking (but still process with words) can memorize the script and use it internally. If a client does not process with words, use this script as a starting point to develop a thought process focused on images, music, or any other stimuli the client could use to pull themselves back into the present moment and recognize that the traumatic event is not reoccurring.

Flashback Stopping Script

My name is _____ (*name*). I live in _____ (*home*). Right now, I am feeling _____ (*emotions*). My body feels _____ (*body sensations*). I am remembering _____ (*trauma*). I am experiencing _____ (*description of body reaction*) because of the memory. The memory is not happening in real life right now, but it feels real because it is happening in my mind.

I am in _____ (*location*), and not _____ (*memory*). I can see/hear _____ (*stimulus in current location*). It is _____ (*describe stimulus in intense detail*). The bad thing is not happening right now. I will _____ (*coping skill*) to feel safe until the memory passes.

Autistic Burnout Interventions

It was only in recent years that the field of psychology began recognizing autistic burnout for what it is: a mental health condition that occurs when an autistic individual is so physically and psychologically exhausted from functioning in a neurotypical world that they can no longer mask or cope with these expectations. While many autistic people report that burnout episodes are triggered by masking, autistic people who do not or cannot mask can also experience burnout as a result of inadequate supports and chronic overstimulation. Essentially, they burn out as a result of the chronic stress of living in a world that is not designed to meet their needs.

Researchers previously thought of burnout as a type of "regression" because autistic people who mask might lose this ability during burnout, so they start to display autistic traits in a more obvious way to the people around them. However, many autistic people have said that this does not accurately describe their experience, and it falls into the problematic autism research trap of conceptualizing autistic experiences by how they impact the people around them rather than the autistic person's experience.

Autistic burnout can trigger depressive episodes and even suicidal ideation or behavior, so it is especially essential for any provider working with autistic clients to center and prioritize the client's well-being over getting them "back to normal" or "restoring functioning." It is not healthy or safe to aim to get "back to normal" when "normal" involved the circumstances that caused burnout in the first place. This will only put the autistic person back in harm's way and could trigger another round of burnout in the future.

Instead, a neurodiversity-affirming approach to treating autistic burnout seeks first and foremost to create a safe space for the client to heal and recover at their own pace. It also seeks to identify what stressors and environmental factors contributed to burnout, to eliminate those factors, and to create a future where the individual is not forced to revert to the behaviors and patterns that brought on burnout in the first place. Although many autistic people who experience burnout are able to recover, some report being unable to fully return to their previous level of "functioning." This suggests that burnout can cause permanent disability, or it might be an indication that the autistic individual was never able to perform at that level in a sustainable way. Since autistic burnout is a newly recognized phenomenon, make sure you keep up to date with emerging research around effective treatment and support. As always, seek out resources by and for the autistic community.

EDUCATION FOR CLIENTS AND CAREGIVERS

ALL AGES

Just like no one is too young to know their diagnosis, no one is too young to receive information about their current mental state and care. While development is often conceptualized by "mental age," this language can be problematic, as it is often used to infantilize autistic people with intellectual disabilities or those who have higher support needs. Accordingly, the following client-focused scripts are presented generally without specific age ranges assigned. Use your clinical judgment to present things in a way that each client can comprehend—considering any preexisting knowledge to inform the rest of the education you provide—and always encourage questions. There is also a script you can use with caregivers when appropriate.

Sample Script for Clients with Less Language Comprehension

You've noticed how some things have gotten harder for you lately. For instance, [*give some specific examples of the client's burnout symptoms*]. These things can happen when someone has dealt with a lot of stress for a long time, and their body and brain just get too tired to keep up.

Remember how we talked about how some things might be harder for you because you're autistic, and your brain doesn't work the same way that the world was designed for? When autistic people become exhausted by trying to keep up with these things, they can experience something called *burnout*. We think that's something you're dealing with now.

Burnout can cause people to get angry or sad more easily, and it can make it more difficult to cope with things, like sounds or textures that bother you. It can make going to school harder too, because things that were already challenging there become even more difficult when you are burned out.

People dealing with burnout need a lot of rest and support. We want to help you so you don't have to feel this way forever. First, we will help you notice when you're having trouble so you can ask for help, and then we'll work on finding ways for you to feel better. What do you think about that? Do you have any questions right now?

Sample Script for Clients with More Language Comprehension

You've shared with me that some things have gotten more difficult for you lately. Specifically, [*share examples of burnout symptoms you have observed*]. Sometimes, those things can be signs of autistic burnout. Are you familiar with autistic burnout? [*Gather information of your client's understanding of burnout and take their preexisting knowledge into consideration.*]

When autistic people experience burnout, they might become irritable or depressed. They might be more bothered by sensory things, and they might have meltdowns or shutdowns more easily. They might be more tired and have trouble doing things that came more easily to them before.

While we don't know everything about burnout, we do know that people who experience burnout can get better. That involves identifying the life stressors and societal expectations that caused them to become burned out in the first place. We can do the same for you—we can identify things in your life that were causing you harm and try to prevent them in the future. What questions do you have about all that?

Sample Script for Caregivers

Recently, we have observed some changes in [*client's*] behavior. [*Give some examples.*] I think they might be experiencing autistic burnout. Is that a term you're familiar with? Autistic burnout is a condition that occurs when an autistic person experiences significant stress over a long period of time. That stress can be caused by masking, or attempting to present as neurotypical even when that does not come naturally, or from the general stress of existing in a world that is not designed for the way that the autistic brain works.

Burnout can look many different ways. It can look like a depressive episode, with sad mood, irritability, fatigue, changes in sleep or appetite, and sometimes suicidal thoughts. It can also look like "regression" or a loss of skills. For example, an autistic person in burnout might not communicate verbally as much or as effectively as they did before, or they might struggle with self-care tasks that they used to be able to complete independently. This regression can occur because burnout causes the loss of certain skills, or it could be that the autistic person was doing that skill independently before even though it was hurting them.

One important thing we need to talk about as [*client*] recovers from burnout is what that recovery will look like. Since burnout is caused by stress and unhealthy masking, we need to identify the ways that their environment, as well as the expectations we put on them, contributed to burnout. Without making changes in these areas, they will just become burned out all over again. However, some autistic people are unable to return to their pre-burnout level of functioning. We need to make sure that [*client*] understands that you love and support them, even if their needs change permanently. Just because they were able to survive in unhealthy conditions before does not mean they should be expected to do that again. If going "back to normal" is not healthy, then it is inappropriate for us to make that [*client's*] goal.

I want to take some time right now to address your concerns for [*client*]. What questions do you have?

CHANGING YOUR ENVIRONMENT

AGES 12+

Burnout treatment cannot be successful if it aims to bring the client back to their pre-burnout baseline, as that baseline likely included the factors that caused burnout in the first place. As the client comes out of burnout, it is important to determine what factors in their environment contributed to their chronic stress and overwhelm. This should include a discussion of factors that drain them, stress them out, and overstimulate them. Encourage them to share these insights with you so that you can help them tweak their environment to better meet their sensory needs.

If the client is unable to identify any environmental irritants, you can make suggestions or use guided questioning to come up with potential examples that are relevant to them. For example, you might educate the client about how many autistic people are more aware of sounds compared to nonautistic people. This can include sounds such as the air conditioning or heater, appliances, or even the electricity in the room. Do they notice any sounds that no one else seems to be aware of? Maybe those sounds are causing a problem. They can try spending time in a quieter environment and see how it impacts how they feel. Of course, this will involve some trial and error, and you can gain just as much information from the things that do not work as the things that do.

The following are some common examples of environmental irritants for autistic individuals, though this is not an exhaustive list, and clients will differ largely in their experience:

- Too bright or too dim lighting
- Too much noise or bothersome noise
- Lack of available comfort items
- Too much activity or movement

Use this information as a template for structuring a sensory space the client can use for self-regulation and recharging. As much as possible, use it to also change the client's larger environment to better meet their sensory needs and foster recovery. This can be an important component of ensuring that their burnout does not get worse. At the same time, you will likely have to reassess the environment as they recover as a preventive measure.

YOU KNOW YOUR LIMITS

ALL AGES

Since autistic people often receive the message that they need to push past their limits in order to conform to neurotypical standards, it may take some time and effort to learn what these limits are and to start to honor them. However, it can be painful for a client to recognize their limits if the people in their life continue to disrespect them. Sometimes caregivers struggle with the concept of limits and want to encourage the autistic person to "just try." This is counterproductive, and this pattern likely contributed to the development of burnout in the first place.

Get caregiver buy-in by educating them about burnout using the information presented earlier in this section, and make a plan with them to honor the client's self-reported boundaries. You will also want to have a session with the client and caregiver together in which you and the caregiver both express to the client that you understand how they are struggling and how they have some limitations that might be different than in the past. Come up with mouth words or a nonverbal signal that the client can use to indicate that they are nearing their limit, and set up a plan for how the caregiver will respond to that communication. The caregiver must consistently follow this plan to show the client that they are trustworthy.

If the caregiver expresses concern that the autistic person will "use this as an excuse" or be dishonest about their limits to "get out of" an expectation, let them know that this is preferable to exacerbating burnout. The most important thing the caregiver can do is give the client space to rest and heal, and second to that is fostering healthy communication and attachment. For both goals, it is vital that the caregiver listen to the autistic person and honor their limits without question. This fosters burnout recovery as well as insight into their needs and limitations.

FINDING YOUR RECHARGE

All tasks consume energy, both tasks we enjoy and tasks that we do out of necessity. When an autistic person has masked for most of their life in an effort to meet neurotypical expectations, they might not know which things they truly enjoy and which things they have been told they "should" like. The interoception activities in this book are a good starting point for bringing awareness to their authentic self, versus what has been forced upon them.

When in burnout, the autistic person has limited energy and resources to get through the day. It is even more important during this time that they use that energy on things that refill their cup as much as possible. To help your client identify what recharges them, have them compile a list of activities that leave them with a sense that they have replenished themselves. For example, perhaps they enjoy spending time with a pet or playing a specific game on a tablet. Prioritize these activities, and help your client craft a schedule that carves time out for these activities every day.

It may be helpful for the client to use the following *Recharging Log* to keep track of which activities most benefit them. They can check in with themselves before and after doing the activity to determine whether it was helpful in reducing their level of stress and making them feel refreshed. However, because burnout can cause fatigue and significantly limit one's energy to do various tasks, this log should only be implemented if the client has the capacity to complete it. The guardian or caregiver can also help with this, if appropriate.

Recharging Log

Date and Time	Emotional Check-In (Before)	Recharge Activity	Emotional Check-In (After)

BACK TO BASICS

Autistic burnout stems from exhaustion. Imagine you are expected to climb a mountain every day, and you have no training or experience. Everyone around you seems to take to the task without issue, and if you ask for help, you are accused of being "difficult" or "lazy" and told to "just try harder." So, day after day, you climb without proper equipment or support, until you hurt yourself. Once you get hurt, it's not a matter of not knowing how to climb safely—it has become physically impossible to even attempt to climb. But no one understands that you are injured because they do not believe it is possible to become injured doing something so simple, something everyone does every day, so you are criticized even more for "regressing" and told to carry on.

Just as with the mountain example, burnout occurs when an autistic person overextends themselves for too long. Attempting to "walk it off" or power through only makes things worse. Therefore, the treatment for burnout is not about trying to force functioning. It is about reducing pressure, expectations, and responsibilities as much as possible while the person recovers. To do so, work with your client (and, if applicable, their guardian or caretaker) to make a list of daily tasks and responsibilities. Go through it together and identify areas where the load can be reduced. Anything that is not required for survival should be reduced to take pressure off the autistic person so they can rest. If possible, they may benefit from reducing work hours or even taking a leave of absence. (In a perfect world, this option would be available to everyone, but of course finances often make this impossible. If the individual is evicted for not paying rent, this will not help their burnout.)

With regard to hygiene tasks, if your client does not have the bandwidth to complete these regular routines every day, this is okay. You can educate them about what tasks are necessary to prevent bigger problems in the long term versus which ones are they can sidestep for now. For example, dental health connects to heart health, so while it is important that they continue trying to brush their teeth, they can let other hygiene tasks go (e.g., showering or changing clothes daily, putting on deodorant) to preserve their energy. If teeth brushing is overstimulating, they can try alternatives that reduce the risk of disease and feel more manageable, like using an alcohol-free mouthwash. If your client experiences any feelings of shame or guilt around their inability to complete any tasks, reframe these thoughts by reminding them that they are caring for themselves appropriately.

REMEMBERING YOUR SKILLS

AGES 6+

When recovering from burnout, it is not enough to help the client build up an arsenal of coping skills; they must also remember what skills to use when the need arises. Every brain works differently, so each client will need to figure out what system is the best for them, but here are some suggestions to try:

- **Use an app.** There exist several apps that help you track skills and tools to help with emotion regulation and coping skills. Some that have free versions include:

    - **Calm Harm:** Helps individuals ride out urges to self-harm with mindfulness skills.

    - **Dare:** Offers a list of coping skills for various emotions and situations. It prompts the user to try different, specific skills if they are unsure what they want to try to calm themselves down.

    - **Finch:** Allows individuals to create and name a virtual critter or buddy who prompts them to engage in daily self-care tasks.

    - **Virtual Hope Box:** Helps individuals put together a collection of specific skills, images, songs, memories, and quotes that they find calming for use when they are struggling.

- **Use phone notes.** Smartphones and tablets contain a notes app where individuals can input written notes as well as links, images, and even scanned documents. Clients can put together an extensive list of coping skills and tools in a pinned note that they can reference at any time.

- **Create a physical toolbox.** For clients who do not have a phone or will not remember to check an app, a physical toolbox containing information about their coping skills can help. This can be a small box containing sensory items and pictures or written scripts about certain skills, a notebook detailing this information, or a scrapbook.

- **Use visual cues.** For clients who struggle with checking their app or using a physical toolbox, it can help to keep visual cues on display in their living space. They might post pictures or sticky notes around the home that cue them to try different skills. This way, they can more easily see coping skills options.

- **Cope on a schedule.** While there will always be moments when an individual needs to engage in a coping skill unexpectedly, it can be helpful to schedule time to practice different skills. This is especially helpful for clients who struggle to notice when they are escalating and need to use skills. Having a predetermined coping schedule can also reduce feelings of embarrassment or shame around needing to de-escalate. While there is nothing shameful about having emotions, anyone might get defensive about needing a coping skill regardless of neurotype. Scheduling skill use ahead of time can help get around this concern.

Requesting Accommodations

Because we live in a society that holds everyone to neurotypical standards and expectations, many autistic people will need accommodations at some point in their lives. Often, mental health providers are the ones providing documentation in order to access these accommodations, so it is important that you understand these requests and know how to best support your clients as they navigate this system. To help you navigate this process, this section includes information about accommodations, accessibility, and disability rights.

Before processing any accommodations requests, always double check that your credentials and scope of practice allow this. It is each professional's responsibility to manage this in their own practice. If you are able to provide requests for accommodations, you can help clients thrive by accessing the support they need. If not, make sure that you have referral information for neurodiversity-affirming providers who can assist with the accommodations request.

Sometimes the accommodations request must come directly from the client or their guardian and not a professional, like a therapist, case manager, or medical doctor. When a client or guardian makes the request themselves, it can foster confidence and autonomy, but the system can be confusing and scary, especially if the individual does not have the knowledge or tools to navigate it. You must balance providing support and fostering autonomy, offering education and resources when appropriate.

The Americans with Disabilities Act

The ADA was signed into law on July 26, 1990, and serves to protect all disabled Americans from discrimination. Information about the ADA, disability rights, and a variety of relevant topics is available at www.ada.gov. Under the ADA, a person with a disability is defined as someone who has "physical or mental impairments that substantially limit one or more major life activities," either currently or historically, or who is "perceived by others as having such an impairment (such as a person who has scars from a severe burn)." A diagnosis of autism spectrum disorder is considered a disability according to the ADA.

Businesses with 15 or more employees are legally required to follow ADA requirements and provide reasonable accommodations for disabled employees, including autistic employees who request accommodations for their disability. "Reasonable accommodations" are adjustments to the job description or work environment that allow a disabled person to do their job effectively. For example, if all work responsibilities can be completed remotely, an autistic person could claim that their sensory issues necessitate remote work as a reasonable accommodation. Employers do not have to provide accommodations that create "undue hardship" or that reduce the quality of work produced.

While a disabled employee will have to disclose that they are disabled in order to request accommodations under the ADA, the employee is still entitled to privacy and confidentiality. As such, the employer cannot ask an applicant about their disability beyond confirming that the employee is able to complete their job requirements. Most employers ask for this information anyway, but the employee can still decline to share their diagnosis when asking for accommodations. As a provider, you can verify that the employee meets the definition for a disability based on the ADA's definition, but you can only provide the client's diagnosis with explicit consent.

Employers are not permitted to retaliate against employees who request accommodations under the ADA or against employees who have filed a complaint. They are also not allowed to tell employees that they are not required to accept accommodations, as this could be coercive. Individuals can file a complaint against any employer who has violated their rights under the ADA.

Disabled college and graduate students also qualify for academic accommodations under the ADA. The institutions are not required to provide equipment but can be required to allow accommodations. For example, a school might not be required to record lectures for students, but a student with an accommodation may not be prohibited from recording the lecture themselves.

While the ADA is intended to protect the rights of disabled people, and it offers a starting point for seeking accommodations (especially in the workplace), it has limitations. First, some terms in the ADA are overly vague, such as what it means for a condition to "substantially limit" an individual or what constitutes "undue hardship" for an employer. In addition, although the ADA prohibits retaliation, most states in America have "at-will employment" laws, meaning that an employer can terminate an employee without reason at any time. Unless the employer says, "We are firing you because you asserted your rights under the ADA," it is often impossible to prove that a firing was a result of retaliation. Even if a client has evidence that the employer engaged in retaliation, it is expensive, stressful, and time-consuming to retain a lawyer and pursue a judgment. Many ADA violations go unchecked because the law is not effectively enforced.

Individuals with Disabilities Education Act

The Education of Handicapped Children Act was originally passed in 1975, and the name was changed to the Individuals with Disabilities Education Act (IDEA) in 1990. This legislation aims to ensure that disabled children receive access to education that meets their needs, prepares them for employment and independent living, protects their rights and the rights of their families, and provides other supports to them and the institutions serving them. Under the IDEA, autistic people enrolled in the public school system who have an official diagnosis on their record qualify for academic accommodations and educational plans that support them in the classroom. It covers people from birth through age 21.

When it comes to accessing accommodations, specific procedures for diagnosis vary. Many school districts require a school assessment in order to document that the child's disability impacts their academic performance or classroom behavior. However, some states and districts will only honor an academic diagnosis. This means that a clinical psychologist who does not work with the school system could do the evaluation and grant a diagnosis, but the district will do their own testing, which may or may not conclude that the criteria are met at school.

Therefore, if a client or their guardian is seeking an evaluation for autism in order to access academic accommodations, have them contact the school's education planning committee, special education department, or principal directly to ask what is required to get accommodations and follow that path. It is not helpful to pay for an evaluation that the school will not accept! If the school accepts a diagnosis from an outside evaluator, have them request this in writing. They can ask if the district will help cover the copay or deductible for the assessment, since the school is supposed to have funds to help with assessments and diagnoses.

If a student qualifies for accommodations, services are delivered through an individual education plan (IEP), which is a document that ensures the individual's unique needs are met in the classroom. It includes input from parents, teachers, other staff, and whenever possible, the student. In addition to spelling out specific accommodations, an IEP includes measurable goals that the school monitors to determine whether the IEP is helping the child progress. IEPs are updated regularly as the child advances, or if it is determined that the current IEP is not meeting their needs.

Rehabilitation Act

The Rehabilitation Act of 1973 is a law that prohibits discrimination against disabled people participating in federally funded programs, including schools. Unlike the ADA, this law only applies in instances when an agency, organization, or program receives federal funding, whereas the ADA applies to most businesses.

Section 504 of this act states: "No qualified handicapped person shall, on the basis of handicap, be excluded from participation in, be denied the benefits of, or otherwise be subjected to discrimination under any program or activity which receives federal financial assistance" (34 C.F.R. Part 104.4). This means that any school, college, or university that receives federal funding is required to provide appropriate accommodations to disabled students.

Under the Rehabilitation Act, disabled students can receive a 504 plan that ensures they have equitable access to the environment at school. It is similar to an IEP in that it provides accommodations, but IEPs are plans focused on advancing the student's education, whereas a 504 plan focuses on access to the environment. Some students have both a 504 plan and an IEP.

Choosing Accommodations

There is no one-size-fits-all approach to accommodations. In fact, if we took a list of every possible accommodation, some would contradict each other. For instance, one student might function best when seated in the front row of the classroom, and another might thrive in the back where they can stim without their peers' eyes on them. Additionally, some accommodations might actually make things worse. For example, sometimes an individual needs to take an exam in a private space so they can focus on what they are doing. Others with the same diagnosis might struggle to focus if they are alone in a room versus in the same space as their classmates.

This is why any accommodation recommendation must reflect the individual's needs and be developed in collaboration with the client. Clients might not know what options are available, so you want to offer suggestions and work together to determine what is the best fit for the client. Often, clients have some idea of what they need or what might help them thrive. If their requests fit within appropriate accommodations, you can make your recommendations based on these requests. Of course, there are limits to what accommodations can be requested—as the ADA states, accommodations must be "reasonable." For example, a student would not be able to request that they simply not be graded at all.

Since clients may feel overwhelmed or not know where to start in requesting accommodations, part of your role is to help them build insight and determine what they need. The following series of questions can help the client explore what kinds of accommodations are the best fit for them:

1. What aspects of school or work are the hardest for you?

2. When do you feel most anxious or nervous?

3. What do you wish were different about your school or work environment?

4. When do you feel rushed?

5. When do you have trouble understanding what is expected from you?

6. What kinds of communication do you understand most easily?

7. What would you change about your daily routine at school or work?

If the client (or their guardian) consents, you can consult directly with the institution from which they are requesting accommodations. The institution can provide information on what reasonable accommodations they are prepared to offer, and you can further clarify their expectations and needs from you.

Sample Letter Templates

Often, employers, schools, attorneys, and insurance companies will request that you submit your full treatment record along with the accommodation request. They might even send you a release of information that your client signed stating that they consent to your sending this information. Before releasing anything, make sure that you speak directly to your client or their guardian about what they have authorized. Many individuals sign a release not realizing how much information is included in treatment notes. This is not informed consent!

As a mental health professional, you must adhere to your ethical codes in all aspects of your practice and know when to release (or not release) client information. This includes ensuring that the client fully understands what is being released, where it is going, and how that information will be used. Your code of ethics also requires that you only release information that is necessary in a given situation. If, for instance, a client is applying for short-term disability, the insurance company does not need the full narrative from their progress notes to confirm that the client qualifies for disability leave. They only need documentation from you that the client meets criteria for a disability.

Since other institutions are not bound by the same ethics codes, they will not care if their request is unethical. It is your job to stick to your ethics and only provide necessary information. The following pages contain letter templates you can use to provide information to the requesting parties without unnecessary disclosure. However, it is important to remember that any accommodation request should meet the specific requirements of the requesting institution. They might request specific information that is not included in a standard template. As always, make sure your client provides informed consent to any information that you submit.

Employer Letter

[*Date*]
[*Your information*]

[*Recipient information*]

Re: [*Client name and date of birth*]

Dear [*recipient*]:

I am [*your name and credentials*]. I am writing this letter at the request of [*client*] to document that they meet criteria for disability accommodations per the Americans with Disabilities Act.

I first met with [*client*] on [*intake date*] and have had [*number of sessions*] on [*dates*]. My assessment of [*client*] includes [*any assessments or tests administered*]. It is my professional determination that [*client*] has a disability that necessitates workplace accommodations.

Specifically, [*client*] has difficulty with [*brief summary of limitations caused by the client's diagnosis*]. As such, [*client*] requires the following accommodations:
[*List of accommodations*]

If you have any questions or concerns about this letter, you can contact me at [*your contact information*]. Thank you for your time.

Respectfully,
[*Signature and credentials*]

School Letter

[*Date*]
[*Your information*]

[*Recipient information*]

Re: [*Client name and date of birth*]

Dear [*recipient*]:

I am [*your name and credentials*]. I am writing this letter at the request of [*client*] to document that they meet criteria for disability accommodations per the Americans with Disabilities Act, the Individuals with Disabilities Education Act, and the Rehabilitation Act.

I first met with [*client*] on [*intake date*] and have had [*number of sessions*] on [*dates*]. My assessment of [*client*] includes [*any assessments or tests administered*]. Per this assessment, [*client*] meets criteria for [*diagnosis*], which entitles them to academic accommodations.

Specifically, [*client*]'s diagnosis of [*diagnosis*] causes [*detail specific difficulties and limitations caused by the disability*]. As such, [*client*] requires the following accommodations:
[*List of accommodations*]

If you have any questions or concerns about this letter, you can contact me at [*your contact information*]. Thank you for your time.

Respectfully,
[*Signature and credentials*]

Final Note

As mental health providers, we commit to offering care that is in line with the best practices in our field. Unfortunately, historic definitions of "best practices" have overlooked client well-being in favor of forcing them to change based on societal values and expectations, or prioritizing the convenience of others rather than the client's true needs. This is particularly true of the autistic community.

Although progress is slow, the field of psychology fortunately seems to be heading in a positive direction. Thanks to organizing efforts within the autistic community, many have made their needs heard and shared their experiences of harm within the field. Professionals who want to offer best practices and the most ethical care to their clients want to listen to these voices and implement necessary change.

By reading this book, you have shown your commitment to offering neurodiversity-affirming care. You are taking an active role in changing the field into something you can be proud of, something that truly helps your clients rather than forcing them into neurotypical boxes regardless of the cost. Thank you.

Resource List

In this section, you will find a variety of books, organizations, blogs, and learning tools to further enhance your knowledge of autism, autistic people, the autistic community, and neurodiversity-affirming care. While I prioritized resources made by autistic people about their experience, this was not an absolute rule-out for inclusion in the list. Nonautistic people can and do provide neurodiversity-affirming care and elevate the voices of autistic people in their work. Additionally, some autistic people (even those in mental health who specialize in helping other autistic people) do not always publicly disclose their diagnosis, which is their right. In some cases, they might be autistic and not realize it. Some people might not feel safe being open about their neurotype. Others might simply prefer to keep this information private. For those reasons, I did not require that authors and creators be openly autistic for inclusion in this list.

In compiling this resource list, I reached out to other autistic people to determine what resources they had found beneficial or had created themselves. Search engines tend to prioritize resources that uphold the historical problems found in autism research, so I was mindful to seek out resources from a broad range of autistic voices, including those with different support needs, communication styles, cultural backgrounds, races, and gender identities. This does not mean I successfully created a list that amplified all experiences. I encourage you to add to this list with any voices I overlooked or was not aware of.

Additionally, no resource is perfect or beyond critique (including this book!). I tried to include tools that will benefit autistic people and the folks who support autistic people. There is likely criticism out there for many of these resources, and I tried to take that into account when creating this list. However, if I were to only include resources that have no negative feedback, criticism, or room for improvement, I would end up with no resources to share. As Voltaire said, "The perfect is the enemy of the good."

All that to say, vet these resources yourself and determine which tools will most effectively enhance your neurodiversity-affirming practice. Make recommendations to your clients based on what they report they need and your professional opinion on the resources themselves. And keep your own database of resources up to date with new options as they become available.

Books

The ADHD & Autism Unmasking Workbook by Emily Oliver

This workbook specifically targets masking behavior that can lead to burnout. It provides readers with tools to identify masking and learn how and when it is safe to unmask, as well as skills for unmasking and self-care.

The Adult Autism Assessment Handbook by Davida Hartman, Tara O'Donnell-Killen, Jessica K. Doyle, Maeve Kavanagh, Anna Day, and Juliana Azevedo

While this book is intended for providers who assess and diagnose autism, it is written in a way that is accessible to nonprofessionals who want to better understand autism and autism assessment. It provides neurodiversity-affirming information about autism, evaluations, and the firsthand experience of living as an autistic person.

All Cats Are on the Autism Spectrum by Kathy Hoopmann

This children's book provides introductory education about autism featuring photographs of cats, light humor, and information about autistic traits. It highlights autistic strengths while not downplaying struggles. It is a good resource for parents teaching their children about their diagnosis.

All the Weight of Our Dreams: On Living Racialized Autism edited by Lydia X. Z. Brown, E. Ashkenazy, and Morénike Giwa Onaiwu

This collection of poetry, essays, fiction, and other art was created by 61 writers and artists from around the world. All contributors are autistic people of color expressing and sharing their unique experiences.

And Straight on Till Morning: Essays on Autism Acceptance by the Autistic Self Advocacy Network

Collected and edited by the Autistic Self Advocacy Network, this book is filled with essays written by and for autistic people. It includes information about autism "awareness" campaigns and helpful information on how to provide neurodiversity-affirming care and support the autistic community effectively.

Beyond Behaviors: Using Brain Science and Compassion to Understand and Solve Children's Behavioral Challenges by Mona Delahooke

While not specific to autism, this book explores traditional responses to behavior problems in children and reframes these responses from a neurodiversity-affirming standpoint. Specifically, it teaches how to address children's needs rather than attempting to punish away "bad" behavior.

The Brain Forest by Sandhya Menon

Although this book is not autism specific, it is a children's book that celebrates neurodiversity and highlights the unique strengths that can come with embracing different neurotypes. It provides concrete ways to create neurodiversity-inclusive spaces.

But You Don't Look Autistic at All by Bianca Toeps

This book is part research (describing the science behind autism) and part memoir (recounting the author's firsthand experience as an autistic person). It addresses myths and facts about autism and describes how nonautistic people can support autistic loved ones.

Color Texture Taste by Matthew Broberg-Moffitt

This cookbook includes 46 recipes as well as information about how to prepare food for people with sensory or dietary issues that make it difficult to find appropriate food. Since autistic people often have sensory issues that interfere with eating, or medical issues that restrict their diets, this book teaches readers how to change recipes to meet texture and visual needs as well as gluten-free or vegan diets.

Dating While Autistic: Cut Through the Social Quagmire and Find Your Person by Wendela Whitcomb Marsh

This guide offers practical advice for autistic adults trying to get into the dating world, with a neurodiversity-affirming approach to addressing social and communication challenges.

A Day with No Words by Tiffany Hammond

This picture book provides education about nonspeaking communication, AAC tools, and the experiences of autistic people who do not use mouth words to speak. It is a resource for parents, teachers, and providers who want to help educate children.

Different, Not Less: A Neurodivergent's Guide to Embracing Your True Self and Finding Your Happily Ever After by Chloé Hayden

This memoir is shared from the perspective of an autistic person with ADHD who is learning to embrace her differences. The story uses humor and emotion when sharing both the author's personal story and practical tips for managing challenges that can come with being autistic.

Divergent Mind: Thriving in a World That Wasn't Designed for You by Jenara Nerenberg

This book explores how neurodivergence, including autism, ADHD, synesthesia, and sensory processing issues, manifests in women—helping to address research gaps that traditionally focus on male presentations and experiences. It includes firsthand stories by those with lived experience of neurodivergence.

The Edge of the Playground: Two Stories, One Journey by Mary Lynn Ackerman Willis and Mikhaela Ackerman

This book shares the story of an autistic girl from the perspective of the child and her mother as they navigate a world that does not offer adequate support. It shows how the child exceeds expectations of an overly pathologizing medical system.

I Am Autistic: A Workbook: Sensory Tools, Practical Advice, and Interactive Journaling for Understanding Life with Autism (By Someone Diagnosed with It) by Chanelle Moriah

This colorful workbook is a wonderful resource for autistic people who want to better understand themselves. It includes educational information as well as self-guided sections to foster self-understanding and acceptance.

I Am the Rainbow and the Rainbow Is Me by Alice McSweeney

This rhyming children's book takes a neurodiversity-affirming approach to educating autistic girls about their neurotype. It uses a strengths-based perspective to promote healthy self-esteem.

Ido in Autismland: Climbing Out of Autism's Silent Prison by Ido Kedar

The autobiographical essays and papers in this collection are all written by a nonspeaking autistic person sharing his experience with communication. He aims to provide accurate and helpful information about the autistic experience from someone who does not speak with mouth words.

Independent Living with Autism: Your Roadmap to Success by Wendela Whitcomb Marsh

This guide offers concrete tips for young autistic adults managing the transition into adulthood. It is designed both for those with a medical diagnosis and those who suspect they may be autistic.

Is This Autism? A Guide for Clinicians and Everyone Else by Donna Henderson and Sarah Wayland

This book is designed to help identify autistic individuals who mask and tend to fly under the radar, going undiagnosed. It presents the diagnostic criteria from a neurodiversity-affirming perspective and has a companion guide called *Is This Autism? A Companion Guide for Diagnosing*.

I Will Die on This Hill: Autistic Adults, Autism Parents, and the Children Who Deserve a Better World by Meghan Ashburn and Jules Edwards

This book aims to bridge the divide between autistic adults and parents of autistic children in response to historic conflict and defensiveness between these two communities. It includes contributions from a diverse group of autistic adults as well as education about affirming care for autistic people and their loved ones.

Knowing Why: Adult-Diagnosed People on Life and Autism edited by Elizabeth Bartmess

This book is a collection of essays written by autistic adults who learned they were autistic in adulthood. It covers a variety of topics, including burnout, sensory overload, special interests, and other topics relevant to the community. It is written for those who were diagnosed as adults and those who are questioning whether they might be autistic.

Learning from Autistic Teachers: How to Be a Neurodiversity-Inclusive School edited by Rebecca Wood

This collection of essays provides information for creating an affirming environment within the school system, with an emphasis on experiences of autistic teachers and staff. It shows how to offer inclusion, understanding, acceptance, and intersectionality for autistic children and staff in schools.

Looking After Your Autistic Self: A Personalised Self-Care Approach to Managing Your Sensory and Emotional Well-Being by Niamh Garvey

This book is written by an autistic author and includes specific tips to cope with sensory and emotional overwhelm while unmasking. It serves as a guide for autistic adults who want to unmask and receive appropriate support.

Loud Hands: Autistic People, Speaking by the Autistic Self Advocacy Network

This book is a collection of essays written by autistic individuals for the autistic community. It includes information about the neurodiversity movement, the history of autism, and current resources. It also highlights individual autistic experiences.

My Autistic Fight Song: My Battle into Adulthood and the Workplace by Rosie Weldon

This memoir shares the story of an autistic adult diagnosed later in life, with her journey to understand herself and her brain. It shares how she handled the various challenges that come from living in a world that does not meet her needs.

My Mummy Is Autistic: A Picture Book and Guide About Recognizing and Understanding Difference by Heath Grace and Joanna Grace

This children's book is coauthored by a mother and son and told from the perspective of the nonautistic son. It shares the child's understanding of his autistic mother, including how they differ when it comes to their brains and communication styles. It also includes educational information for children.

NeuroTribes: The Legacy of Autism and the Future of Neurodiversity by Steve Silberman

This book provides information on the history of autism research and describes how our knowledge and conceptualization of this neurotype has shifted. It looks at the concept of neurodiversity as a whole and makes a case for neurodiversity-affirming care for autistic clients as well as those with ADHD, dyslexia, and other forms of neurodivergence.

Our Journey: A Journal for Parents and Carers to Gather Their Thoughts While Navigating a Young Person's Autism Assessment Journey by Cara Lee

This book, authored by an autistic woman with ADHD, serves to help caregivers through the process of their loved one's autism assessment.

Parenting While Autistic: Raising Kids When You're Neurodivergent by Wendela Whitcomb Marsh

This parenting book is designed specifically for autistic parents, both those whose children are also autistic and those with nonautistic children. It addresses the unique parenting challenges that autistic people experience and provides a neurodiversity-affirming approach to these challenges.

The Reason I Jump: The Inner Voice of a Thirteen-Year-Old Boy with Autism by Naoki Higashida

The author of this book is a 13-year-old nonspeaking boy with autism, who uses an AAC device to share his experience and answers questions about autism and communication.

Relating While Autistic: Fixed Signals for Neurodivergent Couples by Wendela Whitcomb Marsh

This guide provides specific tips and communication strategies for couples in which one or both partners are autistic. It helps bridge communication gaps and differences to facilitate healthy romantic relationships.

Resources for Autistic Adults by Ashley Lauren Spencer

This book is written by an autistic adult to help other autistic adults find and utilize resources that can help them. It addresses a variety of topics, including accommodations, self-help, and "life hacks" designed especially for autistic people.

Sensory-Being for Sensory Beings: Creating Entrancing Sensory Experiences by Joanna Grace

This book explores what it means to be a "sensory being" with sensory-seeking or sensory-avoidant behavior. It provides concrete information for those who support someone with sensory issues, including but not limited to autistic people.

Sincerely, Your Autistic Child: What People on the Autism Spectrum Wish Their Parents Knew About Growing Up, Acceptance, and Identity edited by Emily Paige Ballou, Sharon daVanport, and Morénike Giwa Onaiwu

This collection of essays represents diverse voices in the autistic community and discusses the joys and challenges of parenting an autistic child, including misconceptions about autism and common mistakes by parents and providers. It includes information from different cultural and gender perspectives, making it accessible to a wide variety of families.

Slipper the Penguin: A Story About Embracing Neurodivergence by Amy Marschall

Written by yours truly, this story shares the journey of a penguin who feels like she's not good enough as a bird because she cannot do things the other birds do, such as fly. She later learns that penguins are perfectly good birds, just in a different way. It serves as a guide for teaching kids about neurodivergence.

Start Here: A Guide for Parents of Autistic Kids by the Autistic Self Advocacy Network

This short guide is written by multiple autistic authors about parenting autistic children. It is created for parents of newly diagnosed autistic children and teenagers and describes how to support autistic kids to help them thrive. It also includes information to help parents find supportive services.

Strong Female Character by Fern Brady

This memoir shares a woman's experience of seeking an autism diagnosis and facing barriers, stereotypes, and sexism that get in the way. It provides insight into how autistic women can present in ways that fly under the radar for professionals.

The Subtle Spectrum: An Honest Account of Autistic Discovery, Relationships, and Identity by Joanna Grace

This memoir shares the story of an autistic woman diagnosed in adulthood who explores her identity with the new understanding of her autism. It seeks to offer support to other autistic people and information for nonautistic people who want to be more supportive.

Underestimated: An Autism Miracle by J. B. Handley and Jamison Handley

This book is coauthored by a nonspeaking autistic teenager and his father about the teenager's journey of learning to communicate via spelling.

Uniquely Human: A Different Way of Seeing Autism by Barry M. Prizant and Tom Fields-Meyer

This book offers a neurodiversity-affirming conceptualization of autism, focusing on the idea that autistic people are fully human even if they are different from nonautistic people. It seeks to reframe the tendency to pathologize "autistic" behaviors and focuses instead on a strengths-based approach to supporting autistic people.

Untypical: How the World Isn't Built for Autistic People and What We Should All Do About It by Pete Wharmby

This book explores the ways in which we have set up society to favor neurotypical brains, needs, and preferences. It looks into how these societal choices harm autistic people and make functioning more difficult. It also explores how we might create a more inclusive world.

Welcome to the Autistic Community by the Autistic Self Advocacy Network

This book is written by multiple autistic adults who describe their experience of being a part of the autistic community. It provides information about different forms of support and community for autistic people, especially those who are newly diagnosed, and their loved ones.

What I Want to Talk About: How Autistic Special Interests Shape a Life by Pete Wharmby

This book provides information on special interests and how they are important to autistic individuals. It can help autistic people better understand themselves, and it can also help friends, partners, caretakers, and family members of an autistic person better understand their loved one.

Workplace NeuroDiversity Rising by Lyric Rivera

This book serves as a guide for businesses and organizations that want to appropriately support neurodivergent employees. It offers general information as well as specific solutions to common problems.

Blogs and Podcasts

Ann's Autism Blog

Ann Memmott is an autism professional who writes about her lived experience as an autistic person as well as her work supporting other autistic individuals: http://annsautism.blogspot.com.

Autism 101

Jeff Owens is an autistic adult who shares information for newly diagnosed or suspected autistic people who want to learn more and process their experience: https://autism-101.com/about.

Autism in Black Podcast

This podcast features "all things Autism in the Black parent experience" and offers education, empowerment, and advocacy: https://www.autisminblack.org/podcast.

Autistic Not Weird

Chris Bonnello is an autistic adult who has taught in both mainstream and special education sectors, and he is an author and autistic advocate. He creates and compiles information for autistic adults and is the researcher behind the Autistic Not Weird survey cited in this book: https://autisticnotweird.com.

Autistic Science Person

Ira Kraemer is an autistic advocate and neuroscientist offering information about their experience to the autistic community and to parents of autistic children: https://autisticscienceperson.com.

Autistic, Typing

Jules Edwards, coauthor of *I Will Die on This Hill*, writes about their experience as an autistic adult as well as a parent to autistic children. They provide resources to share with autistic Black, Indigenous, and other people of color on their blog: https://autistictyping.com.

The Black Autist

T. J. Gordon is an autistic disability and social justice advocate. He writes as a resource for Black autistic people and their parents: https://blackautist.wordpress.com/about.

Black Autistic Kayla

Kayla is a Black autistic disability rights advocate who creates video blogs about her experience as a Black autistic queer woman. She also moderates a community for Black autistic people: https://linktr.ee/blackautistickayla.

Black NeuroQueer Punk

Kris Young is a Black, autistic, bisexual, disabled, trans man. His blog focuses on intersectionality in neurodivergence: https://afroautpunk.wordpress.com.

Faith, Hope, and Love . . . with Autism

Philip is a nonspeaking autistic person. He communicates via typing and AAC, and he writes to educate others about his experience: https://faithhopeloveautism.blogspot.com.

Ido in Autismland

Ido Kedar is a nonspeaking autistic person who was "completely trapped in silence" for the first half of his life before being able to communicate via an iPad and letterboard. He shares his experience fighting to be understood: http://idoinautismland.com.

I've Been Autistic All Along?

Cara Lee maintains this blog and resource database for autistic and ADHD individuals identified later in life. She also shares resources for caregivers: https://www.ivebeenautisticallalong.com.

Jordyn's Rocky Journey

Jordyn is a nonspeaking autistic person who is unable to control many of his body movements. He was not given the resources to communicate until age 13. He shares his experience of learning to express himself as a nonspeaking autistic person: https://jordynsrockyjourney.wordpress.com.

Masha du Toit

Masha du Toit is an autistic fiction writer who also shares resources for autistic adults to better understand themselves and their experiences: https://mashadutoit.com/about-2.

Morénike Giwa Onaiwu

Morénike Giwa Onaiwu is a writer and speaker who has contributed to several books written by and for the autistic community. They additionally share experiences and education about autism and the autistic experience: https://morenikego.com.

Neurodetergent Podcast

While not specific to autism, Neurodetergent is a podcast that seeks to connect and support neurodivergent people. It is run by three individuals, two of whom are licensed mental health professionals and one of whom is autistic: https://podcasts.apple.com/us/podcast/neurodetergent/id1675542037.

Neurodivergent Chat Podcast

Nick hosts the Neurodivergent Chat Podcast, which he launched in 2020 to share information about autism acceptance. He shares: "For this podcast, I follow this solemn pledge to you and only you the viewers, absolute transparency, trust, truth, integrity, and to let you guys know that I am always right by your side!" Topics covered in the podcast include relationships and self-advocacy: https://neurodivergentchatpodcast.wordpress.com.

Neurodivergent Parenting: Think Outside the Box

Elspeth Wylde maintains this blog as an autistic adult and parent of autistic children to share affirming tips and tools for families with neurodivergent parents, neurodivergent children, or both: https://www .facebook.com/ParentingOutsideTheBoxMichigan.

NeuroDivergent Rebel

Lyric Rivera is a nonbinary autistic individual seeking to educate the public about neurodiversity, particularly autistic experiences. They additionally specialize in consulting with businesses who want to make their workplace neurodiversity-inclusive: https://neurodivergentrebel.com.

The Neurodivergent Woman Podcast

Monique Mitchelson and Michelle Livock are both psychologists who host a podcast to provide information about neurodivergent women's experiences. They do not exclusively focus on autistic experiences but frequently have autistic guests on their podcast, and they cover a variety of important topics: https://www.ndwomanpod.com.

Not an Autism Mom

Meghan Ashburn is the coauthor of *I Will Die on This Hill* and a speaker and blogger. She is not autistic but is the mother of autistic children, and she works to provide neurodiversity-affirming resources to other parents who feel lost or stuck: https://notanautismmom.com.

Parenting Decolonized

Yolanda is a conscious parenting coach, social justice instructor, and single mother. She offers resources on activism and decolonization in parenting, including internalized ableism and systems issues that harm BIPOC neurodivergent children and their parents: https://parentingdecolonized.com.

Pete Wharmby

Pete Wharmby is an autistic writer, author, and speaker who has worked with many organizations to promote acceptance and understanding of autistic experiences: https://petewharmby.com.

Uniquely Hari

Hari Srinivasan is an autistic disabled person who blogs about education, advocacy, and supporting autistic people by emphasizing both strengths and challenges: https://uniquelyhari.blogspot.com.

Unmasked Autistic

Glenn is a late-diagnosed autistic person who writes about his experiences and seeks to improve understanding and acceptance of autistic experiences: https://theunmaskedautistic.com.

Organizations

Autism in Black

Autism in Black is an organization that supports Black parents of autistic children through educational and advocacy services. It provides parenting coaching, couples couching, and information on IEPs and navigating the school system. Maria Davis-Pierre, the president and CEO of Autism in Black, also shares her own experience as the parent of an autistic child: https://www.autisminblack.org.

Autistic Self Advocacy Network

ASAN is an organization run by autistic adults for the autistic community with the goal of making society inclusive and accessible to autistic people. It works by providing legal advocacy, distributing educational resources, developing advocacy tools, and offering leadership training: https://autisticadvocacy.org.

Autistic Women and Nonbinary Network

AWAN is a nonprofit organization committed to equity, liberation, and disability justice. It offers support, community, and education about autism created by and for the autistic community, including autistic individuals from marginalized genders and identities. It additionally helps with fundraising and financial support for those who need it: https://awnnetwork.org.

Communication FIRST

Communication FIRST is a nonprofit organization dedicated to disability justice and advocacy for nonspeaking individuals. While it does not exclusively work with the autistic community, it offers support to nonspeaking autistic individuals, including education and AAC resources: https://communicationfirst .org.

Genius Within

Genius Within offers neurodiversity-affirming resources and training for those who want to make their organization more inclusive to neurodivergent individuals, including autistic individuals. It additionally offers education and support for neurodivergent individuals looking for support in order to thrive: https:// geniuswithin.org.

Thriving Autistic

Run by volunteers, Thriving Autistic is a nonprofit organization aimed at promoting human rights for neurodivergent people, particularly the autistic community. It aims to provide intersectional and affirming resources for neurodivergent people of all races, genders, and other identities: https://www .thrivingautistic.org.

Additional Resources

The #ActuallyAutistic Coach

Matthew offers individual and group support to autistic people who want to understand themselves better and connect with other autistic people. He specializes in helping autistic individuals unmask and recognize their authentic selves: https://www.theautisticcoach.com.

The Art of Autism

This nonprofit organization is a platform for autistic artists, poets, and writers that seeks to empower autistic people through creative expression and art: https://the-art-of-autism.com.

Ask Me, I'm an AAC User

This private Facebook group is volunteer-run and provides space to ask questions about AAC use. While not autism specific, the group provides answers to specific questions about their experience with AAC so that those hoping to learn more can listen directly to the community. https://www.facebook.com /groups/456220758119314

Ask Me, I'm Autistic

This private Facebook group is volunteer-run and provides space to ask questions about autism and autistic experiences. All questions are presented to autistic volunteers who provide education from a neurodiversity-affirming standpoint: https://www.facebook.com/groups/askautistics.

Autism and Neurodivergence Infocards/Communication Cards

Daniela Schreiter, also known as Fuchskind, is an autistic artist who creates stories and comics, including stories featuring autistic protagonists. She has created communication cards for neurodivergent individuals who struggle with verbal communication at times or who are nonspeaking. The cards are available for free on her website: https://www.danielaschreiter.com/?lang=en&nav=download.

The Autism Pastor

Dr. Lamar Hardwick is a pastor and author of multiple books on the intersection of disability and religion. He provides support for autistic children and young adults, as well as consultation and education about autism: https://autismpastor.com.

Autistic Innovator

Ashley Lauren Spencer is an autistic entrepreneur who created an online store of stim toys and other sensory items intended specifically for autistic adults. She additionally writes books and journals for autistic adults: https://shop.autisticinnovator.com.

The Autistic OT

Sarah Selvaggi Hernandez is an autistic Deaf occupational therapist, author, and speaker. She was the first openly autistic elected official in the United States. She offers education about autism and sensory issues as well as workshops, trainings, and other resources to support autistic culture: https://theautisticot.com.

Autistic Realms

Helen developed this neurodiversity-affirming organization to provide support and resources to autistic people and their families, including burnout guides, education about language, and neurodiversity-affirming resources: https://www.autisticrealms.com.

Autistic Studies

River, an autistic adult, built Autistic Studies to be a community for autistic adults and their loved ones to highlight autistic-led research and education about autism: https://www.autisticstudies.com.

Brightfire CIC

This organization was created with the intention of connecting autistic people to each other, embracing autistic identities, and empowering autistic people to have fulfilling and healthy lives. It offers individual and group support, as well as a wealth of resources about autism: https://www.brightfirecic.com.

DisABILITY Resources Toolkits (DART)

The American Psychological Association has published a portfolio of tools and educational information about disability rights and accommodations: https://www.apa.org/pi/disability/dart.

Divergent Thinking Collective

This online community is run by a licensed therapist known as "the AuDHD Therapist" who seeks to educate the public about neurodiversity and neurodivergence. The collective provides support groups and counseling, and the AuDHD Therapist is working on video classes to provide neurodiversity-affirming education about ADHD and autism: https://divergent-thinking.com.

Embrace Autism

Described as "the ultimate autism resource," Embrace Autism was founded by Dr. Natalie Engelbrecht and Eva Silvertant. The website offers extensive educational information about autism from a strengths-based and neurodiversity-affirming standpoint. Individuals who suspect they may be autistic can take free screening assessments to learn more and see if they display autistic traits: https://embrace-autism.com.

Fidgets and Fries

Tiffany Hammond is an autistic speaker, consultant, parent, and advocate. She offers a wealth of resources about autism, disability, and anti-racism, and she provides expert consultations for organizations that want to do better in these areas: https://www.fidgetsandfries.co.

How to Get On

This website details resources for seeking and obtaining support for disabilities in the United States. While it was designed for physically disabled people, the information included can benefit autistic people who need assistance (and autistic people who are also physically disabled): https://howtogeton.wordpress.com.

Inside Our Autistic Minds

This limited series from the BBC offers a documentary from the perspective of autistic people about their experiences: https://www.bbc.co.uk/programmes/p0bbnjvx.

Mask Off

Lauren is a business development consultant seeking to raise awareness and acceptance of autism and ADHD in BIPOC communities. She fights against stigma and promotes neurodiversity-affirming approaches to mental health, especially around gender and racial disparities: https://maskoffcic.com.

The Megalist of Potential Neurodivergent Accommodations

Kate Kowalczik is a licensed clinical social worker who put together a list of accommodations that neurodivergent individuals, including autistic individuals, might find beneficial. The list breaks down accommodations by the type of need and provides information about making requests for accommodations: https://drive.google.com/file/d/1Pc3lHc4ybIArl_SRUdfF33IIMT-icWbm/view

National Alliance on Mental Illness

NAMI is a mental health organization developed by and for individuals with a variety of mental health issues. Although this is not an autism-specific resource, it supports autistic people who have a comorbid mental health diagnosis and offers resources around autistic support needs: https://www.nami.org.

NeuroClastic

NeuroClastic is an online publication by and for the autistic community, offering an endless list of resources and firsthand accounts of autistic experience and support. The founders make a point of elevating marginalized autistic voices, including the Black community and nonspeaking autistic people: https://neuroclastic.com.

Neurodivergent Practitioners Directory

This directory features therapists, coaches, evaluators, and other providers who have committed to a neuro-affirmative practice. All providers also commit to being LGBTQ+ affirming and anti-racist: https://neurodivergentpractitioners.org.

Neurodivergent Therapists

This is a therapist directory where all listed providers identify as neurodivergent and agree to follow specific values, including honoring neurodiversity, cultural competency, and social justice: https://ndtherapists.com.

So, You're Autistic?

This resource offers education and support for autistic people, for those who suspect they are autistic, and for those awaiting an assessment. The group works to educate the public about autism from a neurodiversity-affirming standpoint and fight stigma: https://soyoureautistic.com.

Spellers

This documentary tells the story of nonspeaking autistic people learning to communicate through spelling. It includes stories directly from autistic individuals who use this technique to communicate: https://spellersthemovie.com.

Supernova Momma

Natasha (Tash) Nelson is a certified positive discipline educator and parenting expert working to help parents provide an affirming and supportive environment for their children. She is autistic and has two autistic children, and she often shares personal experiences to educate her followers. She provides classes to help parents implement positive discipline and positive parenting: https://supernovamomma.com.

Thinking Person's Guide to Autism

TPGA is an online resource aimed at providing accurate information about autism and elevating autistic voices in sharing their stories. The website contains resources for autistic people and their loved ones: https://thinkingautismguide.com.

This Is Not About Me

This documentary shares the story of Jordyn Zimmerman, a nonspeaking autistic person who struggled to communicate in a way that others could understand. It shares her journey, including her experience being institutionalized and finally finding the support she needed to communicate: https://thisisnotaboutme .film.

Worldwide Autists

This "friendship group for autistic adults" offers autistic-led support groups on six continents and in multiple languages. It aims to help autistic adults find and support each other: https://worldwideautists .com.

Glossary of Terms

504 plan: An education plan for a disabled individual to ensure that they receive accommodations to support academic success in elementary or secondary education settings.

ableism: Discrimination against someone based on disability or discrimination that favors able-bodied people.

accommodations: Alterations to the environment, curriculum, equipment, or job description allowing a disabled person to access the environment or complete tasks.

agender: An adjective describing a person who identifies as not having any gender.

allistic: A person who is not autistic.

Americans with Disabilities Act (ADA): A law passed in 1990 that prohibits discrimination against disabled individuals in all public areas of life.

applied behavior analysis (ABA): A behavioral therapy that seeks to understand and modify behavior. It is often used to train autistic people to mask in unhealthy ways.

Asperger's syndrome: A diagnosis that has since been retired and refers to autistic individuals who did not experience significant language delays in early development. This term is sometimes associated with "high-functioning" autism.

assessment: In psychology, the measures used to determine a diagnosis or someone's mental health status.

autigender: A term used by some autistic individuals who inherently experience gender or sexuality through their autistic neurotype.

autism: A diagnosable neurotype in the *DSM* in which an individual experiences social, behavioral, and sensory stimuli in a way that is fundamentally different from neurotypical norms.

autistic: An identity-first term for someone who meets criteria for autism; the preferred term for approximately 80 percent of autistic adults. (*See also* identity-first language, person-first language.)

autistic burnout: Extreme physical, mental, and psychological fatigue experienced by autistic people. It is brought on by unmanageable stress and marked by a reduced ability to manage personal needs, sensory experiences, and interpersonal communication. (*See also* burnout.)

autistic community: All autistic people.

autonomy: The human right to control one's own life, circumstances, and body.

burnout: Physical, mental, or psychological fatigue brought on by ongoing stress but not necessarily marked by impairments or loss of skills. (*See also* autistic burnout.)

collateral data: Information gathered for an assessment from an individual other than the identified client—for example, by interviewing caregivers, guardians, or partners. (*See also* self-report.)

communication skills: The ability to express one's needs and thoughts effectively, in a way that others can understand.

comorbid diagnosis: When an individual has more than one disorder, disability, or disease at the same time.

conservatorship: A legal order that appoints an individual to control and have guardianship over someone who is deemed incapacitated. Conservators often control financial affairs and can also be in charge of medical and personal decisions.

demand avoidance: The inability to do certain things for oneself or others, which can manifest as distractibility, withdrawal, meltdowns, or refusal. (*See also* PDA.)

disability: Any physical or mental condition that limits an individual's activities, sensory experiences, independence, or other areas of functioning.

disorder: A physical or mental condition that is considered abnormal or atypical.

flashback: An intrusive, vivid memory of a traumatic event that can feel like the event is reoccurring.

food aversion: A strong dislike or inability to consume a certain food, a type of food, or many types of food, due to the sight, smell, texture, or taste.

functioning: One's ability to manage independent life skills without assistance.

gaslighting: Psychological abuse aimed at making an individual question their sanity by attempting to manipulate or invalidate their perception of reality, memories, and experience.

genderfluid: An individual whose gender shifts or changes over time.

guardianship: A position in which someone is legally responsible for another individual's well-being and choices. Parents are typically guardians of minor children, and courts can place adults in legal guardianships if they deem the adult unable to make their own decisions or care for themselves independently.

identity-first language: Language that centers the identity before the person (e.g., "autistic person"). (*See also* person-first language.)

individual education plan (IEP): A plan developed by an educational institution to ensure that a disabled child receives special instructions and services. These plans require measurable growth goals.

Individuals with Disabilities Education Act (IDEA): A law in the United States that requires appropriate public education be freely available to all children, regardless of disability.

interoception: The ability to sense and interpret internal signals from one's body.

losing speech: When an individual loses the ability to speak, sometimes due to stress or injury.

masking: Hiding or disguising autistic traits in order to present as neurotypical, often done to meet neurotypical standards of behavior. (*See also* unmasking.)

meltdown: A response to overstimulation or overwhelm in which an autistic person loses control of their behavior and can become verbally or physically aggressive toward themselves or others.

mindfulness: A mental state in which one nonjudgmentally focuses awareness on the present moment or one's own internal experiences.

mouth words: Words spoken out loud using one's mouth.

neurodivergence: When an individual's brain diverts from neurotypical expectations.

neurodivergent: An individual whose brain functions outside of neurotypical expectations.

neurodiversity: The vast range of ways in which a brain can develop, function, and perceive the world.

neurodiversity-affirming: Care that acknowledges the variety of neurotypes and does not center one neurotype as inherently superior to others.

neurotype: The way in which an individual's brain functions.

neurotypical: An individual whose brain functions within expected, typical standards for society.

nonautistic: An individual who is not autistic. (*See also* allistic.)

nonbinary: An individual whose gender does not fit into the male/female binary.

nonspeaking: The inability to produce language through speech.

nonverbal: The inability to comprehend verbal language.

overstimulation: A state where an individual experiences sensory stimuli to an excessive degree, causing sensory overload.

overwhelm: A state of becoming overstimulated by stressors or the current environment.

PDA: Referred to as "pathological demand avoidance" in some literature and "persistent drive for autonomy" in neurodiversity-affirming circles, this term refers to patterns of behavior in which an individual avoids anything perceived as a demand or deliberately does the opposite of what an authority figure requests. (*See also* demand avoidance.)

person-first language: Language that centers the person rather than the identity (e.g., "person with autism"). (*See also* identity-first language.)

pervasive developmental disorder: A term for a neurodevelopmental diagnosis that is no longer in use, referring to an individual who experiences unspecified developmental delays that impede functioning in various areas.

regression: A loss of skills that an individual previously possessed.

Rehabilitation Act: A United States law that prohibits discrimination on the basis of disability in any program that receives federal funding.

safe food: A food that an autistic person enjoys, which gives them a positive sensory experience and brings a sense of happiness or comfort.

same food: A food that an autistic individual frequently eats over and over.

self-care: Practices that preserve physical and mental health and well-being.

self-report: Information collected directly from the individual. (*See also* collateral data.)

sensory-avoidant: A tendency to avoid a particular sensory experience that an individual finds unpleasant.

sensory-seeking: A tendency to seek out a particular sensory experience that an individual finds enjoyable.

shutdown: Withdrawal occurring as a result of sensory overstimulation or stress.

social skills: The way that an individual interacts and communicates with others following specific societal rules and styles. Traditional social skills training tends to focus on neurotypical standards for interaction and relationship building.

stigma: Negativity associated with a particular quality, diagnosis, or type of person.

stim: Movements, sounds, and other behaviors done repetitively or ritualistically to aid in self-regulation.

stimming: The act of engaging in stimming behavior.

transgender (trans): An individual whose gender is different from the gender they were assigned at birth.

trauma-informed care: An approach to healthcare that acknowledges that many patients and clients have trauma history, which is not always disclosed, and that takes steps within the organization to prevent further traumatization.

trigger: A stimulus that brings up memories or sensory experiences related to a trauma or other stressful event or situation.

unmasking: The process of showing one's authentic and true self. (*See also* masking.)

References

For your convenience, purchasers can download
and print the worksheets in this book from
pesipubs.com/marschall_autistic_clients

American Psychiatric Association. (2022). *Diagnostic and statistical manual of mental disorders* (5th ed., text rev.). https://doi.org/10.1176/appi.books.9780890425787

Angell, A. M., Empey, A., & Zuckerman, K. E. (2018). A review of diagnosis and service disparities among children with autism from racial and ethnic minority groups in the United States. In *International Review of Research in Developmental Disabilities* (Vol. 55, pp. 145–180). Elsevier. https://doi.org/10.1016/bs.irrdd.2018.08.003

Arnold, S. R., Higgins, J. M., Weise, J., Desai, A., Pellicano, E., & Trollor, J. N. (2023). Confirming the nature of autistic burnout. *Autism*. Advance online publication. https://doi.org/10.1177/13623613221147410

Autistic Self Advocacy Network. (2020, June 25). *Ending guardianship: How state governments take away our right to make choices and how we can stop it.* https://autisticadvocacy.org/actioncenter/issues/choices/guardianship

Aylward, B. S., Gal-Szabo, D. E., & Taraman, S. (2021). Racial, ethnic, and sociodemographic disparities in diagnosis of children with autism spectrum disorder. *Journal of Developmental & Behavioral Pediatrics, 42*(8), 682–689. https://doi.org/10.1097/DBP.0000000000000996

Baer, R., Crane, C., Montero-Marin, J., Phillips, A., Taylor, L., Tickell, A., & Kuyken, W. (2021). Frequency of self-reported unpleasant events and harm in a mindfulness-based program in two general population samples. *Mindfulness, 12*(3), 763–774. https://doi.org/10.1007/s12671-020-01547-8

Bloom, S. L. (2010). Organizational stress as a barrier to trauma-informed service delivery. In M. Becker & B. A. Levin (Eds.), *A Public health perspective of women's mental health* (pp. 295–311). Springer.

Böhnlein, J., Altegoer, L., Muck, N. K., Roesmann, K., Redlich, R., Dannlowski, U., & Leehr, E. J. (2020). Factors influencing the success of exposure therapy for specific phobia: A systematic review. *Neuroscience & Biobehavioral Reviews, 108*, 796–820. https://doi.org/10.1016/j.neubiorev.2019.12.009

Bonnello, C. (2022, October 4). *Results and analysis of the Autistic Not Weird 2022 Autism Survey.* Autistic Not Weird. https://autisticnotweird.com/autismsurvey

Bottema-Beutel, K., Kapp, S. K., Lester, J. N., Sasson, N. J., & Hand, B. N. (2021). Avoiding ableist language: Suggestions for autism researchers. *Autism in Adulthood, 3*(1), 18–29. https://doi.org/10.1089/aut.2020.0014

Chadwick, P. (2014). Mindfulness for psychosis. *British Journal of Psychiatry, 204*(5), 333–334. https://doi.org/10.1192/bjp.bp.113.136044

Chapman, R., & Botha, M. (2023). Neurodivergence-informed therapy. *Developmental Medicine & Child Neurology, 65*(3), 310–317. https://doi.org/10.1111/dmcn.15384

Conners, C. K. (2022). *Conners 4th edition manual.* Multi-Health Systems.

Goldstein, S., & Naglieri, J. A. (2009). *Autism Spectrum Rating Scales.* Multi-Health Systems.

Haruvi-Lamdan, N., Horesh, D., Zohar, S., Kraus, M., & Golan, O. (2020). Autism spectrum disorder and post-traumatic stress disorder: An unexplored co-occurrence of conditions. *Autism, 24*(4), 884–898. https://doi.org/10.1177/1362361320912143

Hutson, T. M., McGhee Hassrick, E., Fernandes, S., Walton, J., Bouvier-Weinberg, K., Radcliffe, A., & Allen-Handy, A. (2022). "I'm just different—that's all—I'm so sorry . . .": Black men, ASD and the urgent need for DisCrit Theory in police encounters. *Policing: An International Journal, 45*(3), 524–537. https://doi.org/10.1108/PIJPSM-10-2021-0149

James, E., Harvey, M., & Mitchell, R. (2018, May 16). *Accessible summary: The big bedtime audit.* Centre for Disability Research. https://wp.lancs.ac.uk/cedr/2018/05/16/the-big-bedtime-audit-evening-routines-in-the-community

Kalb, L. G., Singh, V., Hong, J. S., Holingue, C., Ludwig, N. N., Pfeiffer, D., Reetzke, R., Gross, A. L., & Landa, R. (2022). Analysis of race and sex bias in the Autism Diagnostic Observation Schedule (ADOS-2). *JAMA Network Open, 5*(4), Article e229498. https://doi.org/10.1001/jamanetworkopen.2022.9498

Kleinhans, N. M., Johnson, L. C., Richards, T., Mahurin, R., Greenson, J., Dawson, G., & Aylward, E. (2009). Reduced neural habituation in the amygdala and social impairments in autism spectrum disorders. *American Journal of Psychiatry, 166*(4), 467–475. https://doi.org/10.1176/appi.ajp.2008.07101681

Kupferstein, H. (2018). Evidence of increased PTSD symptoms in autistics exposed to applied behavior analysis. *Advances in Autism, 4*(1), 19–29. https://doi.org/10.1108/AIA-08-2017-0016

Lai, M.-C., Lombardo, M. V., Auyeung, B., Chakrabarti, B., & Baron-Cohen, S. (2015). Sex/gender differences and autism: Setting the scene for future research. *Journal of the American Academy of Child & Adolescent Psychiatry, 54*(1), 11–24. https://doi.org/10.1016/j.jaac.2014.10.003

Lai, M.-C., & Szatmari, P. (2020). Sex and gender impacts on the behavioural presentation and recognition of autism: *Current Opinion in Psychiatry, 33*(2), 117–123. https://doi.org/10.1097/YCO.0000000000000575

Leask, J., Leask, A., & Silove, N. (2005). Evidence for autism in folklore? *Archives of Disease in Childhood, 90*(3), 271. https://doi.org/10.1136/adc.2003.044958

Local Government Association. (2023). *Sound: Considering and meeting the sensory needs of autistic people in housing.* https://www.local.gov.uk/our-support/partners-care-and-health/autistic-and-learning-disabilities/autistic/housing/sound

Mantzalas, J., Richdale, A. L., & Dissanayake, C. (2022). A conceptual model of risk and protective factors for autistic burnout. *Autism Research, 15*(6), 976–987. https://doi.org/10.1002/aur.2722

North Dakota Department of Health and Human Services. (2022). *Autism spectrum disorder (ASD) database.* https://www.hhs.nd.gov/autism-spectrum-disorder-asd-database

Payne, P., Levine, P. A., & Crane-Godreau, M. A. (2015). Somatic experiencing: Using interoception and proprioception as core elements of trauma therapy. *Frontiers in Psychology, 6.* https://doi.org/10.3389/fpsyg.2015.00093

Powell, R. (2014). Can parents lose custody simply because they are disabled? *GP Solo, 31*(2), 14–17.

Raymaker, D. M., Teo, A. R., Steckler, N. A., Lentz, B., Scharer, M., Delos Santos, A., Kapp, S. K., Hunter, M., Joyce, A., & Nicolaidis, C. (2020). "Having all of your internal resources exhausted beyond measure and being left with no clean-up crew": Defining autistic burnout. *Autism in Adulthood, 2*(2), 132–143. https://doi.org/10.1089/aut.2019.0079

Rumball, F., Happé, F., & Grey, N. (2020). Experience of trauma and PTSD symptoms in autistic adults: Risk of PTSD development following *DSM-5* and non-*DSM-5* traumatic life events. *Autism Research, 13*(12), 2122–2132. https://doi.org/10.1002/aur.2306

Sandoval-Norton, A. H., Shkedy, G., & Shkedy, D. (2019). How much compliance is too much compliance: Is long-term ABA therapy abuse? *Cogent Psychology, 6*(1), Article 1641258. https://doi.org/10.1080/23311908.2019.1641258

South, M., Costa, A. P., & McMorris, C. (2021). Death by suicide among people with autism: beyond zebrafish. *JAMA Network Open, 4*(1), Article e2034018. https://doi.org/10.1001/jamanetworkopen.2020.34018

Späth, E. M. A., & Jongsma, K. R. (2020). Autism, autonomy, and authenticity. *Medicine, Health Care and Philosophy, 23*(1), 73–80. https://doi.org/10.1007/s11019-019-09909-3

Stein, S. (2019, March 29). *Organ transplant disability bias gets second look under Trump.* Bloomberg Law. https://news.bloomberglaw.com/health-law-and-business/organ-transplant-disability-bias-gets-second-look-under-trump

University at Buffalo. (2022, October 24). *What is trauma-informed care?* https://socialwork.buffalo.edu/social-research/institutes-centers/institute-on-trauma-and-trauma-informed-care/what-is-trauma-informed-care.html

Van Diest, I. (2019). Interoception, conditioning, and fear: The panic threesome. *Psychophysiology, 56*(8), Article e13421. https://doi.org/10.1111/psyp.13421

Warrier, V., Greenberg, D.M., Weir, E., Buckingham, C., Smith, P., Lai, M.-C., Allison, C., & Baron-Cohen, S. (2020). Elevated rates of autism, other neurodevelopmental and psychiatric diagnoses, and autistic traits in transgender and gender-diverse individuals. *Nature Communications, 11*, Article 3959. https://doi.org/10.1038/s41467-020-17794-1

Wilkenfeld, D. A., & McCarthy, A. M. (2020). Ethical concerns with applied behavior analysis for autism spectrum "disorder." *Kennedy Institute of Ethics Journal, 30*(1), 31–69. https://doi.org/10.1353/ken.2020.0000

About the Author

Amy Marschall, PsyD, is a licensed clinical psychologist who obtained her degree from the University of Hartford. She currently owns her private practice, RMH Therapy, where she provides therapy and psychological evaluations. She specializes in trauma-informed and neurodiversity-affirming care, rural mental health, and telemental health. She has expertise in diagnosing ADHD and autism, as well as in supporting these individuals in an affirming way. She is licensed in Florida, Montana, New York, North Dakota, South Carolina, South Dakota, and Wisconsin, as well as New Zealand.

Dr. Marschall regularly consults with tech companies to make assessment and mental health services more accessible, particularly diagnostic evaluations for autistic adults and those with ADHD. She is the clinical director of A Change for Better and the chair of the clinical committee at the ACFB Fund, a charitable organization that funds mental health services. She also teaches continuing education through PESI, Spring Health, the Telehealth Certification Institute, and A Change for Better on a variety of topics, including telemental health, trauma, and neurodiversity-affirming care. She is the author of the following books:

- *Telemental Health with Kids Toolbox*
- *Telemental Health with Kids Toolbox, Volume II*
- *Clinical Documentation with Children and Adolescents*
- *I Don't Want to Be Bad: A CBT Workbook for Kids, Parents, and the Professionals Who Help Them*
- *Armani Doesn't Feel Well: A Book to Help Sick Kids*
- *Sometimes Vera Feels Scared*
- *Slipper the Penguin: A Story About Embracing Neurodivergence*
- *A Year of Resiliency: 365 Journal Prompts to Become Your Strongest Self*

Dr. Marschall is the proud human of two cats, Armani and Vera. She is autistic and has ADHD. Some things are hard for her, but hyperfocus is her superpower, as long as her husband helps her remember to eat lunch.